The Bridgnorth Infirmary

James Milman Coley
(1784–1867)
Surgeon, Physician, Author
&
Founder of the Bridgnorth Infirmary

CONTENTS

Afflictions sore long time I bore
Physicians all were vain
till God was pleased to give me ease and free me from my pain.

St Mary Magdalene Churchyard, Quatford, Shropshire

HYGIENE is the only useful part of medicine,
and hygiene is rather a virtue than a science.

Jean-Jaques Rousseau (1712–1778)

Quality is never an accident,
it is always the result of intelligent effort.

John Ruskin (1819–1900)

To understand God's thoughts we must study statistics,
for these are the measure of His purpose.

Florence Nightingale (1820–1910)

Be careful about reading health books.
You might die of a misprint.

Mark Twain (1835–1910)

Preface

I first entered the portals of the Bridgnorth and South Shropshire Infirmary as a child in the days when the Matron would entertain the senior staff and their families at Christmas. Thereafter I entered, like many another resident of Bridgnorth and its environs, as a patient; then as a voluntary nursing auxiliary during a school holiday, to see if I could withstand the sights, sounds and smells of hospital life prior to eventually commencing training as a State Registered Nurse (SRN). This title of SRN became obsolete decades ago, as did the role of the hospital matron, whose position of authority permitted me, several years later, to work at the Infirmary prior to further post-registration training.

Many years later I returned to Bridgnorth where my interest in local history grew, as did my desire to discover more about the founding and development of the Infirmary. A visit to the Bridgnorth library and its local studies section produced a single document entitled *Bridgnorth Hospital*. Consisting of four single-sided A4 sheets, neatly typed, that were neither signed nor dated, the contents of this anonymous paper did, however, suggest the existence of primary documents. Here, then, was scope for further research.

Enquiries then led me to the late Miss Jean Hawker, SRN, Matron and subsequently Nursing Officer (1974–89) of the Bridgnorth and South Shropshire Infirmary. On a cold February day in 1999 I learnt from Miss Hawker that she had researched and compiled *A Short History of Bridgnorth's Hospitals* (1996), the proceeds of which had been donated to the Infirmary's League of Friends. I also learnt that primary documents did exist in the form of the 'Hospital Records'. A contact name was given: Mr Kevin Moore, General Manager of the Bridgnorth Hospital (as it is now called). A formal approach was made and through Mr Moore's assistant, Carol Harris, the documents were gradually located at a time of much upheaval due to the commencement of (yet more) building works – a feature of the Infirmary from its inception. I was then privileged to remove the records on what has proved to be an extended loan of considerable duration!

Enthralled by their contents, which raised many questions, I chose to continue my search. This led, inevitably, to the Shropshire Records and Research Centre (now the Shropshire Archives) and a wealth of information in the form of minute books and other material. But where should I start? It was then that I decided to enrol on a course in 'Research in Local History' at the University of Birmingham, which proved invaluable. Now more informed, visits to Shrewsbury Archives and other centres took place, as did letter writing to various institutions which, in turn, assisted in either locating, or failing to do so, further material in my search for more information.

During the period covered, 1832–1920s (with a brief résumé in the epilogue to 1948, when the Infirmary became an integral part of the National Health Service), it is clear that the micro-history of the Bridgnorth Infirmary reflected, in part and often belatedly, the many developments in medicine, nursing, hospital design and public health. As a consequence an attempt has been made to reflect those changes through the use of referenced material, so that others, if they so choose, may further their reading or indeed enlarge upon my study.

There was also the desire to correct a particular anomaly, namely the founding year of the hospital. This was 1835, and not 1841 as reported in *Kelly's Directory* and other directories, and since perpetuated in a national report (1993), a local history publication (1998) and the chronological boards of Bridgnorth's town hall. Why was 1841 considered to be the founding year? The answer lies in a minute book where a clear copperplate hand has written: 'Bridgnorth Infirmary Established 1841'. However, prior to this date a number of issues arose of such magnitude that they necessitated, in today's parlance, a re-branding exercise. These issues required exploring, particularly as they concerned James Milman Coley, medical man and self-declared founder of the Infirmary, and his dispute with others at the Infirmary during the years 1838–1840.

There are two sides to every story and various facts emerged from the minute books that offered an administrative perspective. A search for Coley's perspective, particularly his pamphlet entitled *A Faithful Report of the Late Disgraceful Proceedings at the Bridgnorth Infirmary* and other papers, proved elusive. Some material was found, which added another piece to the jigsaw, but constrained by a lack of material a full picture of the dispute did not emerge. This arguably produced a bias that I attempted to reconcile by opining on what might have happened. However, in early 2015 a friend offered to undertake a worldwide search, and in so doing found Coley's *Faithful Report* languishing in the medical history library at Yale University, USA! – a joyous moment made real by an assistant librarian who arranged for me to have a scanned copy.

Amongst the Hospital Records there are various other documents, including a copy of a nineteenth-century Ordnance Survey map upon which is written: '1822 plan showing the infirmary an infectious disease hospital' [*sic*]. The map is the Ordnance Survey of 1884 (Bridgnorth, lviii 8.17) showing the Union Workhouse, which was built in 1850 and subsequently known as Innage House. As a workhouse, included amongst its buildings were an infirmary, a casual ward for itinerants and an infectious diseases hospital that served the destitute of Bridgnorth and surrounding parishes. As such, its purpose was quite distinct from that of the Bridgnorth Infirmary, which was a voluntary hospital whose purpose was to serve the sick poor and servants of the bourgeoisie. Consequently the Union Workhouse Infirmary is not considered here. Similarly, there are three documents relating to 'The Society for the Relief of poor Married Women in Childbed'. Dated 1819 to 1821 inclusively, they relate to the Parish of St Leonard. As maternity cases were excluded from the Bridgnorth Infirmary and as midwifery has its own history, this subject is also excluded.

So what is included? Particular attention has been given to the early years of the Infirmary from its inception in 1832 to 1840. Thereafter a period of consolidation occurred. However, other changes are also considered, namely the inadequacies of the Infirmary building which, in the 1880s, led to agitation for a new building on a more accessible site. After 61 years to the month, a new infirmary was formally opened in 1896 in an area known as North Gate (today written as Northgate). With the introduction of the National Insurance Act (1911) another contentious issue arose that affected not only those working men who subscribed to the health insurance scheme but also the two 'imported' panel doctors who were appointed to enable the Act to come into force. Viewed by three Bridgnorth GPs, who were also honorary surgeons to the Infirmary, the two panel doctors were perceived as strike-breakers, and as a consequence both the panel doctors and their patients were denied access to the Infirmary's beds and services for a number of years. Another moment in the Infirmary's history was during the First World War, when it was designated an Auxiliary Military Hospital from 1915 to 1918, receiving financial support from the War Office until 1919 when payments ceased (thereby creating considerable financial difficulties for all concerned). There was also, at this time, an inability to attract nursing and domestic staff. However, whether this was related to the financial situation or other causative factors, such as the exclusion of the panel doctors and their patients or women seeking alternative employment opportunities, remains unclear.

Such changes and contentious issues are perceived as major events in the life of the Infirmary. In addition there was always a constant struggle for survival where dependence upon philanthropy to remain financially viable was partially reliant upon the land-owning classes and those associated with the Infirmary's purpose, such as subscribers and Friendly Societies. Others in the community also played their part by organising fund-raising events. However, such charitable giving rarely covered the Infirmary's expenses and one can only admire those who consistently endeavoured, over the decades, to keep the doors of the Infirmary open through the voluntary efforts of charity: a notion that is difficult to comprehend today, living as we do cocooned within a Welfare State.

Inevitably there are gaps in the story, and doubtless there are errors too (these will all be mine), but my intention to provide a fuller picture, particularly of the Infirmary's early years, has been partially fulfilled.

Gillian Waugh Pead
Bridgnorth, 2017

Acknowledgements

This self-imposed study of the Bridgnorth Infirmary has been long in the making and could not have been accomplished without the willing co-operation of many individuals and representatives of various organisations, societies, trusts and public bodies.

I am, in the first instance, truly indebted to Mr Kevin Moore, previously General Manager of the Bridgnorth Hospital, for allowing me to hold, on loan, the historical records of the Bridgnorth Infirmary over a period of time that has extended well beyond expectations! To Carol Harris, personal assistant to Mr Moore, for locating the various records having been distributed throughout the hospital during yet more building works. Special mention must also be made of three general practitioners who once practiced in Bridgnorth, for their willingness to provide information and encouragement: the late doctors David Ashcroft, Michael Barritt, David T. Binns and his late wife Barbara. Thanks must also go to Dr Bill Hammerton, retired and in rude health, for the loan of early medical publications, and for his introduction to Mrs June Spinks whose researches of a family member, Dr A. Weir, identified a connection to Doctor William Thursfield, senior, of Bridgnorth.

To Mrs Ann Doherty, previously Practice Manager of the Northgate Medical Practice, and to her successor, Ms Sandra Sutton, for their willing and proactive co-operation, and for liaising with the Practice Partners, who allowed access to their boardroom, thus enabling me to photograph the only known picture of Dr James Milman Coley. Thank you.

To The Lady Forester, DL and Trustees of the The Lady Forester Trust whose administrator, Mrs J.E. Gorman, gave me admirable assistance: my sincere thanks for allowing unfettered access to the Trust's archives that are privately held at Willey Park.

There are also two individuals whose support has proved invaluable, namely Susannah Stapleton (who located Dr Coley's *Faithful Report*) and Dr Richard Moore, both of whom, during their own respective researches, not only alerted me to material but also, on occasion, provided me with relevant documents the contents of which often added another piece to the jigsaw.

Thanks must also be extended to all the Trustees of the Bridgnorth and District Historical Society and particularly the late Mr Ken Perkins who, as the voluntary curator of the society's Northgate Museum, allowed me to browse through documents rather than to dust! To his present successor, Mr Richard Batho and volunteers, a further thank you for their co-operation, and in searching out, much to my relief, a particular document that I had inadequately recorded.

It's always a delight to make contact with descendants of relatives whose names appear in documents and of whom one has no knowledge, so for a fuller picture of these persons I am indebted to Mrs Barbara M. Loudon whose great-aunt was

Matron, Miss Frances 'Fanny' Hadfield; Mr John Piper whose grandmother's family, the Wilmotts, rented No. 18 North Gate from the Apley Estate; and Mrs Ann Kerr whose great-grandfather was Doctor William Rhodes of North Gate House.

Sincere thanks are also extended to Mrs Linda Widdows and Mr Don Fullwood of The League of Friends of Bridgnorth Hospital for their help and willingness to meet with me (in the Friends' coffee shop) on a number of occasions to respond to queries and verify ownership of the pictures that I wished to use in this book. There are others too in the local community who, having expressed an interest in what I was doing, have alerted me to material and much else besides, so thank you to: Sue Burns, Ann Chadwick, Gwynne Chadwick, Max MacKenzie, Judy Nagle, Toby Neal, Val Pedrick, Tony Rickards, Jane Smith, Elizabeth Stenning, Mary Tipton, Joan Lawrence, Ann Walter, Dr Connie Wan, Chris Wright, and all my fellow volunteers at the Bridgnorth Library Local and Family History Centre. Nor should I forget Mrs Emma Spenser, Branch Manager of the Bridgnorth Library, who has consistently but quietly encouraged me to get published; thank you Emma! Three other people who should not be forgotten are the late John Hares, Jean Hawker and Margaret Rutter, all of whom, in their respective ways, have contributed to Bridgnorth's local history.

Fulsome praise must also be heaped upon archivists, curators, librarians, registrars and, in more recent times, assistants and volunteers, for their courtesy, guidance and co-operation at the: Birmingham City Archives, Bridgnorth Library, British Medical Association Archive, British Red Cross Museum and Archive, Derbyshire Record Office, Guildhall Library (manuscripts section), Historic England, Ironbridge Gorge Museum Trust Library and Archive, Judge Samson Ltd., Kidderminster Reference Library, Llandudno Library, London Metropolitan Archive, Ordnance Survey, RIBA Architectural Library, Royal Birmingham Society of Artists Archive, Royal College of Nursing, Royal College of Physicians, Royal College of Surgeons (Edinburgh), Royal College of Surgeons of England, Shropshire Archive, Shropshire Regimental Museum, Telford District Land Registry, University of Birmingham Barnes Library, University of St Andrews Special Collections Library, Wellcome Trust History of Medicine Library, Worshipful Society of Apothecaries of London Archive and Yale University Cushing/ Whitney Medical Historical Library.

I also wish to extend my sincere thanks to Alannah Tomkins, Professor of Social History at Keele University and to Malcolm Wanklyn, Emeritus Professor of Regional History (whose knowledge of Bridgnorth is extensive), for not only their encouragement but also their reading of an initial draft and for their critical comments and helpful suggestions which I have endeavoured to fulfil if, I fear, only partially! Then there are those at Logaston Press and particularly Andy Johnson, for his willingness to 'take me on' and for his introduction to Richard Wheeler whose excellent editorial abilities have vitalised and perfected my text with the support of Su Wheeler, all of whom, without exception, have assisted in bringing my book to fruition. I am, as ever, thankful for your patience, guidance and professional support. At this point, mention should also be made of my efforts to locate copyright holders and photographers of images reproduced within these pages. Should any further information come to light I, and the publisher, would greatly appreciate being informed so that corrections, in any future reprints, could be acknowledged. And last but not least to my very patient husband, Michael, who has suffered many a burnt offering as I laboured, often in vain, to get my thoughts onto paper; if I had a wish it would be that he was a chef so that I might write to my heart's content! Finally, if I have inadvertently omitted anyone, please accept my most sincere apologies.

Gillian Waugh Pead

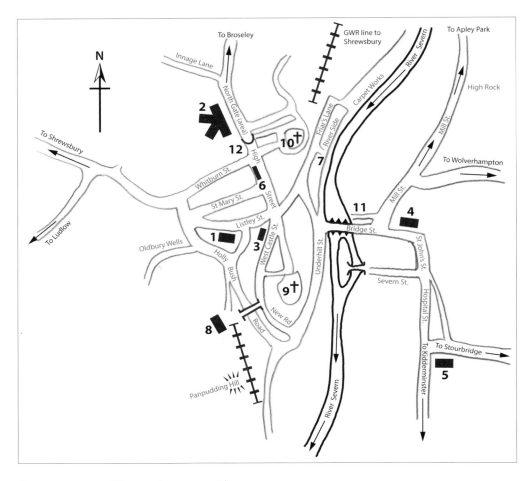

Bridgnorth Town (*not to scale*)

1. Bridgnorth Infirmary (1836–96), Holly Bush Rd.
2. Bridgnorth & South Shropshire Infirmary (1896–present), North Gate
3. Site of Bridgnorth Dispensary, West Castle Street
4. Site of The Hospital of the Holy Trinity and St John, St John Street
5. Site of The Hospital of St James, Hospital Street
6. Town Hall, High Street
7. Site of Franciscan Friary, River Side
8. Great Western Railway Station, opened 1862 (now Severn Valley Railway)
9. Church of St Mary Magdalene
10. Church of St Leonard
11. Doctors Lane (allegedly named after the Doctors Coley)
12. North Gate pedestrian and vehicular arches

Introduction

THE ancient market town of Bridgnorth in south-east Shropshire is a town of two parts, an upper part and a lower part. The upper part, or High Town, is perched upon a red sandstone ridge from which the easterly aspect overlooks the valley below where the River Severn bisects the lower town, or Low Town.

Beyond Low Town's eastern bank of the river there once stood two mediaeval hospitals: the Hospital of Holy Trinity and St John, which cared for the elderly and infirm, and the leper Hospital of St James. Nothing remains of these hospitals except for the naming of streets: St John Street and, leading from it, Hospital Street that once led to the leper hospital outside the confines of Low Town. Both of these hospitals were sequestered in the 1530s by the Crown, who subsequently granted the properties to individuals for secular use. This was the fate that also befell the impoverished mendicant Order of Franciscans whose friary once stood on Low Town's western riverbank. How the sick and elderly were served thereafter is for others to explore, but names of later physicians and apothecaries were fleetingly observed in various documents as I attempted to discover, with little success, more information on the dispensary whose founding may have occurred in the latter part of the eighteenth century.

As a charitable institution, funded by subscribers, the dispensary's purpose was to provide free advice, leeches and medicines to the sick poor within the town's two parishes of St Mary Magdalene and St Leonard, providing the attending medical man considered those before him to be 'proper objects' of charity. Those unfortunate to be categorised as 'improper objects' of charity, and therefore excluded from the dispensary, were maternity cases and anyone requiring admission to a hospital for a surgical procedure, including those presenting with a fracture. Such exclusions were not peculiar to Bridgnorth; however, by the early 1830s the charity's efficiency had come into question.

Hence the perceived need by some, including the surgeon Mr James Milman Coley, to erect an infirmary combined with a dispensary where every attention could be given to the impoverished inhabitants of the town and district. Eventually built in

1

High Town in an area outside the town walls known as New Town, the erection of the infirmary proved contentious. This is demonstrated, in part, by correspondence in two provincial newspapers, where italics and capital letters were applied to emphasise certain words. Such a usage has been reproduced within these pages, as has the underlining found in other sources.

Known originally as the Bridgnorth Infirmary, its nomenclature has changed over the decades to reflect its wider purpose. The Infirmary, now the Bridgnorth Hospital, has also had a chequered existence as the threat of closure has loomed large on a number of occasions during the nineteenth and twentieth centuries, and most recently in 2005. On each occasion there was a determination by all concerned, including those in the community, to retain the Infirmary's beds and services, as their absence would require travelling to hospitals outside the district. Such a disadvantage was known to the founders of the Bridgnorth Infirmary, for they too considered the County Hospital at Shrewsbury to be at an 'extreme distance' from Bridgnorth if 'severe accidents, and urgent and acute diseases' were to be treated promptly.

The driving force behind the founding of the Bridgnorth Infirmary was James Milman Coley, a Bridgnorthian and medical man with a vision. This study seeks to follow his realisation of that vision and its perpetuation as a medical charity into the twentieth century.

1 CONFLICTS OF INTEREST

The completion of the beneficent undertaking which we have assembled to commence, will reflect permanent honor [sic] on all who may contribute their aid. We have every prospect of success: a few months only have passed away since the voice of charity was raised.

James Milman Coley, 29 November 1832

A T 12 noon on Thursday, 29 November 1832, a public meeting was convened. The purpose was to consider the desirability of establishing an infirmary in the market town of Bridgnorth, which, combined with the existing dispensary, would offer efficient medical relief to the 'labouring population'.

In the Chair was the sitting Member of Parliament, Thomas Whitmore, Esquire, of Apley Park, whose family, since 1582, had many landed and political interests in the town. However, it was James Milman Coley, a 48-year-old medical man and resident of Mill Street in the Low Town of Bridgnorth, who was invited to address the public. His detailed presentation,[1] supported by factual information, must have been persuasive, for those present resolved that an infirmary should be provided for the town and its environs. As for those who objected to such a plan, Coley was willing 'to receive any advice from the opponents of the measure'.

Coley had already received objections from 'some of the friends of the Salop Infirmary' who allegedly had 'been thrown into a panic', fearing that any infirmary in Bridgnorth 'may withdraw some of its supplies', meaning money. Coley argued that here was proof indeed of the necessity for such an establishment. Surely local people would prefer to support a local institution 'rather than contribute to a distant and extravagant establishment' that had, apparently, cost £16,000 to build and furnish. The cost of the proposed Bridgnorth Infirmary, on the other hand, would 'not exceed 2,000 guineas'. Furthermore, the residents of Shrewsbury and its vicinity should be reminded of the 'large sums' of money that had been taken 'from the southern division of the county' without providing 'adequate advantages'. As Coley bluntly stated: 'In short, if this part of the county should think proper to provide its own establishment, the other can have no right to complain'.

What Coley did not refer to during his address was the dispute that had arisen between the supporters of the Bridgnorth Dispensary and the advocates of the proposed infirmary. And here we turn to the pages of two provincial newspapers, the *Shrewsbury Chronicle*[2] and the *Salopian Journal*[3] – and, in particular, correspondence from two Bridgnorthians to the respective editors of those newspapers. The letters, which were written following the stone-laying ceremony of the Bridgnorth Infirmary in 1835, offer a glimpse of the tensions that existed in 1832 and which had continued up until 1835, and indeed beyond that date. They highlight, to some extent, the discord that occurred between the medical men of the town and the perceived inadequacies of the dispensary. Indeed, at the inaugural meeting of the Infirmary, the Reverend Boulton declared that 'the Dispensary was not a good; it was improperly managed, and had proved a decided failure' in serving the needs of the sick poor.

Dispensaries were charitable institutions where medical men dispensed medicines and proffered advice, free of charge, to the sick poor on an out-patient basis. Medical men – physicians, surgeons and apothecaries who, after 1834, were designated as Medical Officers (MOs) with the introduction of the New Poor Law – also undertook to visit the poor in their homes by prior arrangement, thereby offering a domiciliary service. This was the case at Bridgnorth. Such institutions were financed by subscriptions from subscribers to the medical charity, of which there were 61 in Bridgnorth in 1831. Subscribers could then 'recommend' a patient through 'Letters of Recommendation' or 'Tickets' as they were known locally. In the major cities, dispensaries were open six days a week, Sunday being a day of religious observance. However, in Bridgnorth, the Dispensary was open only on Tuesdays and Saturdays, when attendees were expected to present themselves between 11am and midday in 1830.

Credit for what has been termed the 'Dispensary Movement' is generally attributed to the Quaker and Scottish educated physician, John Coakley Lettsom (1744–1815) who, in 1770, opened the General Dispensary in London.[4] Treatments however were not necessarily conducive to health, as the following contemporary verse demonstrates:

> When any sick man to me apply,
> I physicks, bleeds and sweats 'em,
> If after that they choose to die,
> What's that to me, I Lettsom.[5]

Originally known as Free Dispensaries, from the mid-nineteenth century Provident Dispensaries came into being where contributions of a penny per week were required from those wishing to avail themselves of the service.[6] In Bridgnorth however, at a meeting of the Dispensary subscribers in November 1832, it was agreed that in the following year, 1833:

> *Any Labourer, or other poor person, living in the Town of Bridgnorth, or within seven miles from it, unable to pay a Surgeon adequately from his own means, may be admitted, at any time, an Independent Subscriber, and on paying four Shillings shall receive a Ticket, by presenting which to a Surgeon, himself or any one member of his family, shall be entitled to have Medicines, Leeches, and Advice, for six successive weeks ...* [7]

But such a change in practice, which reflected the notion of self-help, brought forth scathing comments from a correspondent to the *Salopian Journal* in response to a correspondent to the *Shrewsbury Chronicle*. On Friday, 9 October 1835, a Bridgnorth correspondent to the *Shrewsbury Chronicle*, who signed himself 'Old Subscriber and well-wisher to the Dispensary', declared that the 'existing Dispensary' was 'established more than a century ago' (i.e. in *c.*1735) and that up to the present time it was quite sufficient to meet the needs of 'the poorer inhabitants' of the town. The following week, on Monday, 12 October 1835, a response appeared in the *Salopian Journal* from a Bridgnorthian who signed himself 'Philantropos'. Philantropos refuted many of the points in the letter, starting with the date of the founding of the Dispensary, by stating that it had not been in existence 'for more than half a century' (i.e. in *c.*1785). Of the two dates suggested, that of *c.*1785 would appear more appropriate as it is consistent with the development of dispensaries that has been identified by Loudon.[8]

Philantropos also states that: 'at the present there is NO DISPENSARY AT BRIDGNORTH'. But was this the case? Certainly an Annual Report for 1835 exists and lists 63 subscribers, two more than in 1831.[9] There is also a town map of 1835 where a building, located at the north-west end of West Castle Street, is assigned a letter 'D' and given in the reference key as 'Dispensary'.[10] What we find is that the building 'of late years [had] fallen into disuse' as the committee, according to Old Subscriber, considered it a more economical plan to visit the sick in their own dwellings. Philantropos responds with his opinion:

> *the only apartment used for the Dispensary was a small room in a cottage hired from Mr C. Hanbury Tracy at three guineas a year, which has been given up for several years, the patients having deserted it: and when the counter, drawers, gallipots and 'old cakes of roses' were offered for sale by auction, not a single bidder was to be found: and the room being emptied of its contents, has since been occupied as a Catholic Chapel.*

He also poured scorn on Old Subscriber by asserting that it was not the committee that visited the sick in their dwellings but the medical officers, who were also referred to as dispensers in the letters. Another acerbic reminder by Philantropos to Old Subscriber was that: 'if he subscribes to a medical club, believing it to be a Dispensary, his intellect cannot be very bright'. Medical clubs were 'the mutual health insurance organisation of the day'[11] and involved the payment of a few pence per week, which the poor, on low wages and with no savings, simply could not afford.

We also learn from Philantropos that:

> the solitary medical officer was joined by his former opponents ... who readily agreed to unite into a contract to attend, bleed, leech, and physic the poor for the sum of four shillings a-head, with the view of preventing, if they could, the gratuitous attendance and advice, which will be afforded at the Infirmary.

There were also, according to Philantropos, 'at least 11 resident medical and surgical practitioners in the town' five of whom were considered to be 'of note' in 1835. Was it these unnamed five who had colluded with the medical officer (MO), a Mr Joseph Hall, to attend the poor at 4s a-head?

Coley, in his public address of 1832, mentions there being 'six other medical men in the town' apart from himself. From a public notice[12] dated 11 March 1835 entitled 'To the Inhabitants of Bridgnorth and the Neighbourhood' – which relates to the 1815 Apothecaries Act – six 'Apothecaries (commonly called Doctors)' are named in the following order:

Mr Coley, having practiced prior to 1815.
Mr Hall, having practiced prior to 1815.
Mr James Coley, by virtue of his Certificate.
Mr Proud, having practiced prior to 1815.
Mr John Coley, Jun. by virtue of his Certificate.
Mr Seymore [Seymour], by virtue of his Certificate.

All, according to the notice, were 'legally entitled to practice as Apothecaries' in Bridgnorth. There was a seventh name, Mr George Davis, who had apparently delayed producing his Apothecary's Certificate by four months and therefore was in breach of Section 20 of the Act – a penal clause which could lead to a conviction – otherwise 'he would have been entitled to practice as an Apothecary'. But medical men and others often ignored Section 20, and Mr Davis was no exception, being appointed by the Dispensary Committee as one of the surgeons to that institution in 1836.

The Apothecaries Act of 1815 had been introduced to regulate unqualified practice and thereby make a distinction between apothecaries and 'mere' druggists who were perceived, by apothecaries, as threatening their livelihoods. The public notice to the inhabitants of Bridgnorth and the Neighbourhood also included the wording: 'Druggists are merely allowed to compound Prescriptions not to dispense Medicines'. Apothecaries sold drugs, compounded drugs prescribed by physicians and, since the early eighteenth century, had had the right to prescribe drugs on their own initiative.[13] They also provided general medical care to those who sought them out and were the precursor of the general practitioner (GP), a term that came into being around 1812, particularly amongst those medical men who combined the three functions of apothecary, surgeon-apothecary and practitioner of midwifery.[14] The Act also required that all apothecaries should be licenced following a period of study that included a six-month attachment to a hospital. However, the qualification of Licentiate of the Society of the Apothecaries (LSA) 'did not imply any knowledge of anatomy or surgery'[15] and was therefore not held in high regard, particularly by Bridgnorth's senior medical man, Mr James Milman Coley.

Returning to Old Subscriber, he plainly expressed his displeasure regarding the founding of the Bridgnorth Infirmary: it was an unnecessary expense and severe cases of accident, based on Mr Hall's experience, the MO, were extremely rare. The number of cases was also considered to be few (314 are given in the Annual Report for 1835) and as for the County Hospital, it was so near (at 20 miles from Bridgnorth or, as Coley identified, 'in some situations, not less than 30 miles'). Philantropos fulminated: who wants to travel to Salop (Shrewsbury) in a 'jolting cart' with 'a fractured limb' or 'strangulated hernia'?

The entire situation could be remedied, as far as Old Subscriber was concerned, by enlarging the present Dispensary and building baths that would give 'advantage to the sick' and 'benefit the public at large'. But 'plain water baths' are being erected in the Infirmary, retorted Philantropos. Finally, Old Subscriber implored that 'every Gentleman and Lady solicited [should] NOT GIVE MONEY' to the Infirmary charity and concluded his letter with a warning:

> I cannot too strongly recommend the subject to your earnest consideration before it is too late, and I will venture to predict, that should the erection of an Infirmary be persisted in, it will be at last, from want of the necessary funds, be obliged to become subservient to the Dispensary.

But it was too late. The Infirmary was being erected, and as Philantropos had stated earlier, the 'insufficiency' of the Dispensary had 'become so obvious that the Treasurer waited upon Mr. J.M. Coley, to consult him respecting some practicable improvements'.

Hence the meeting in 1832 where it was agreed that an Infirmary, 'united with an extensive Dispensary, was necessary for the increased demands of the poor'.

And so we return to that public meeting in 1832 and the presentation by Mr James Milman Coley, who had assiduously researched his subject. His address, though long and detailed drew, at its opening, 'on the very inefficient aid that was given to the poor, when their health was farmed out to the parish doctors'. Coley also suggested, after describing five harrowing case studies in which patients were either left deformed, disabled or dead, that the poor should be saved from the 'dangers' of such inappropriate cures. Needless to say, these and subsequent remarks about 'parish doctors' did not endear Coley to his medical colleagues who would have provided a part-time medical service, based on the Parish System, under the Old Poor Law of 1601. Continuing, Coley also alerted his audience to the fact that such medical incompetence 'saddled' the parish 'with an enormous expense'. An economic burden that was increasing, both nationally and locally, and one that the better-off, as ratepayers, were obliged to pay. Reason enough, perhaps, for establishing an infirmary where 'every accident and disease' could receive 'the most early and satisfactory attention'.

With such emotive issues now addressed, Coley turned to the practicalities of establishing an infirmary. This included calculations on the number of persons who would require medical relief, estimates of expenditure and income, and proposed inmate (patient) occupancy and staffing levels. To support many of his propositions, Coley also proffered comparisons drawn from other English provincial hospitals and infirmaries, specifically naming Bath, Canterbury, Huddersfield, Manchester, Sheffield and Shrewsbury.

A 'ground plan' of the proposed infirmary was also produced which had been prepared by Mr Josiah Griffiths of Chantry House, Quatford. Described by Coley as an 'architect', Griffiths appears to have been a local architect-builder who had assured Mr Coley that those wards heated with 'warm air' – in practice, open fires – 'would not consume more than seven tons of coal a year'. As for the building itself, the outer walls were to be 14 inches thick and built of Broseley Brick, a distinct product manufactured in Broseley, a town some five miles north of Bridgnorth. Internally, there would be six wards: two on the ground floor for 'accidents' and 'ordinary diseases'; two on the upper storey for 'fevers'; and two others (presumably on the middle floor) for servants, as patients and employees of the well-to-do, not of the institution. Each ward would contain four or five beds as 'of late' it had been considered more 'conducive to health than crowding of a great number together'. The perceived wisdom of the time being that cross-infection – from one person to another in immediate association by air, droplets, towels and other artefacts – would be reduced.

That Coley had stipulated a need for separate 'fever' wards in 1832 is curious, as 'fevers' of all descriptions, including infectious diseases were, as a generalisation, excluded from (general) hospitals. However, the town and indeed the nation had, for the first time since the visitation of the plague, encountered a disease of epidemic proportions: 'Asiatic cholera'. Endemic in the Indian subcontinent, cholera strode unabated across continents to reach England in October 1831. Its arrival caused consternation, not least amongst the medical fraternity, for if cholera were contracted many of its victims would suffer an agonising death within 24 hours. Medical men, who at that time lacked scientific medical knowledge, resorted to their normal practices of bleeding, leeching and other useless cures that doubtless hastened the death of the patient. Meanwhile, many groundless assumptions were being made about cholera, for there were those who considered the causative factor to be miasma (foul-smelling air) whilst others considered cholera to be a contagious disease that was transmitted by physical contact. Such assumptions would, however, not be dispelled until Dr John Snow (1813–1858) reported in 1855 on his now famous epidemiological studies in which he concluded that cholera was a water-borne disease that necessitated improvements in water supplies and sewage disposal. Hence the introduction of a nascent public health service when sanitary reform became the order of the day. In the meantime cholera, which reappeared in the following three decades, would not only engender fear in the population but also not be fully understood until developments in the medical sciences occurred in the 1880s. In response to the epidemic of 1832, the Privy Council ordered Local Health Boards to be established, as at Bridgnorth. Their responsibility was to clean up the environment, which meant that the public were expected to 'ventilate' and clean their dwellings and dispose of 'nuisances', including human and animal excreta, in a responsible manner in the expectation that the cholera would be contained. Empowered by the Cholera Act 1832, activities were to be financed out of the local poor rates.

Bridgnorth, like other towns throughout the land, was an insanitary place. As late as 1849, when cholera reappeared to confound the local Committee of Health, 'nuisances' were variously described as dung heaps, night soil and ashes, mixen, privies, cesspools and pigsties, all of which were deemed offensive and to be found throughout the town.[16] One can only assume that in 1832 conditions were similar, if not worse, including the water supply, which in Low Town and some parts of High Town was untreated and drawn from the River Severn; the remaining parts of High Town being served by spring water from Conduit Field via an 'aquaduct' down Whitburn Street to three cisterns in the High Street.[17] As for the dwellings of the poor, many lived in caves hacked out of sandstone whilst others were 'built into or against the sandstone rock'.[18] That cholera was a disease which created 'excitement' in the town during 1832, not only amongst the poor but also amongst doctors who refused to attend the sick, can be seen from the notice below:

Sir,

  A meeting of the Old and New Board of Health will take place this day, at Six o' Clock precisely, when your attendance is particularly requested, to determine if any representation should be made to the Privy Council as to the disinclination of some of the Medical Gentlemen to attend cases of real or supposed Spasmodic Cholera, and whether in the event of any fatal cases occurring again in this Town, before legal Burial Grounds are provided by the Parishes, the Board would allow the extra expense of a leaden Coffin, in order that the Corpse may be securely interred in the Church-Yards of either Parish, and thus preclude a re-occurrence of the late excitement.

Bridgnorth.
Monday, September 3, 1832.[19]

Was this 'excitement' in the town over 'real or supposed Spasmodic Cholera' another motivating factor to establish an infirmary? Coley was, after all, addressing his audience two months after the above notice had been circulated, and made an oblique reference to it by referring to the 'disgraceful opposition to the Board of Health'.

Through the reported word there is also a glimpse of Coley the man: a pre-Victorian self-made medical man who demonstrated a concern for the poor, for he stated that 'Poverty should only be considered a misfortune'. Such consideration was extended further to include those who had suffered permanent disability through medical 'ignorance' and 'neglect' when poverty then became 'converted into a severe punishment'. His altruism, if that is what it was, also included attending 'more than a thousand' poor annually who chose to 'find their own medicines', such was their poverty or distrust, perhaps, of cures! Yet, like many of his class at this time, there was also disdain for the 'idle', the 'profligate' and particularly those who developed 'artificial diseases' or 'simulated real ones' only to abuse charitable institutions, particularly in the 'winter season'.

Coley also understood the fear that people had of entering hospitals, either as visitors (such as 'benevolent ladies and the clergy') or as patients, which at this time meant the poor. The upper and middle classes were always attended by medical men in their own homes where doctors were expected to make their entrance by the tradesman's door, such was their status in polite society. Seeking to allay the anxieties of those present, Coley assured them that where the wards, including the 'fever' wards, were concerned, care would be taken to 'ventilate the apartments' by opening windows – a new practice that replaced the previous practice of keeping windows closed in hospitals. There would, therefore, be 'little danger of contamination: for the morbific effluvium … is rendered harmless by plentiful dilution'. To any prospective visitors who might 'fear infection' Coley further advised that they should keep their distance and not stay too long.

Turning next to the clergy, Coley suggested that an infirmary could be beneficial to them in their 'pious labours of preparing the weary traveller for his journey to the regions of immortality'. Such a Christian purpose is succinctly explained by Anne Summers:

> *The state of medical knowledge in this period was not such that the sufferer could be assured of recovery. The sickbed might be the last place where the soul could be brought to recognise the necessity and the source of salvation, and be rescued from the pains of hell. Care of the body was not ignored, but its prime importance lay in facilitating the cure of the soul.*[20]

But if visitors feared entering hospitals, the poor feared them even more, for they had to contend with and endure medical practices upon their body (including operations without anaesthesia, as the latter had yet to be discovered), not only in life but, following the passing of the Anatomy Act of 1832, also in death. This legally permitted the dissection of dead paupers by medical students in authorised medical schools. It was an Act, as Bynum remarks, that: 'fuelled public sentiment against doctors' and which 'made the poor less willing to receive treatment in hospitals, for fear they would be experimented upon and dissected'.[21] Hence Coley's later remark that 'in all cases it will be desirable to induce the poor to enter the establishment'.

Coley was a medical man who was also politically aware, for he expounds, with his opinions, on the issues of the day – in particular those relating to poor relief and, expressly, medical assistance. He also comments on the inadequacies of the education and training of apothecaries under the 1815 Act. He makes particular reference to those medical men who called themselves surgeons, for they were required, in Coley's estimation, to be a member of one of the four Royal Colleges of Surgeons, thus indicating some form of education and training in the art.

There was now a delicate matter that required addressing: namely that none of the local medical men, except Coley, had gained membership to a Royal College of Surgeons. Under the 1815 Act, apothecaries became legally entitled to practice surgery, and therefore membership of a Royal College of Surgeons was not a prerequisite to practice. Surgeons, now threatened, raised their teaching standards, and in 1824 stipulated that they would only recognise schools or hospitals in London, Edinburgh, Aberdeen and Dublin. This requirement piqued England's provincial medical men who, due to the expense, could not attend schools of anatomy in London's recognised hospitals. This disadvantage was rectified when schools of anatomy in properly regulated provincial hospitals were recognised by the Royal College of Surgeons in 1832. Meanwhile

London, by the 1830s, had gained a reputation, above the other centres, as an educational centre of excellence at the expense of Edinburgh, whose previously long-held high reputation was tarnished by the activities of resurrectionists (body snatchers), for it was they who supplied anatomists with disinterred bodies for dissection. The 1830s also saw the founding of two new hospitals in London (University College Hospital 1834 and King's College Hospital 1839) in addition to the established teaching hospitals, all of which required lecturers and demonstrators. This demand was largely met by migrating Scots from Edinburgh to London, including John Abernethy (1764–1831), surgeon to St Bartholomew's Hospital[22] where James Milman Coley, under the tutelage of Abernethy, had furthered his medical and surgical education before returning to Bridgnorth.

Because of his apparent medical abilities, Coley, who was a member of the Royal College of Surgeons (London), appears to have had a high professional standing in the community, which presumably extended to fee-paying patients. Perhaps it was not surprising, therefore, that his colleagues 'joined' with the 'solitary medical officer' to fend off Coley's vision of an infirmary, for such a development would doubtless have damaged their earnings. But how were such men to be included in this new venture? At one point in his address, when Coley was referring to staffing levels, he had suggested that at the opening of the infirmary the subscribers should elect two surgeons for life. The essential qualification for such a post, according to Coley, 'universally required [surgeons] to be members of one of the Royal Colleges of Surgeons'. He continued by adding that:

> At Bath, and most English hospitals, the choice is restricted to those belonging to London; and I certainly should give a decided preference for them. At the first appointment of Surgeons to Sheffield Infirmary, it was agreed that they should be chosen from resident practitioners, and I should propose the same proceedings here.[23]

Coley had declared his ambition to be a Surgeon for Life; a position that he would hold, but not for life. As Coley was of the opinion that the qualification of LSA was insufficient to meet the surgical needs of patients, he then declared that he was 'induced to propose the admission of such as have been in practice before 1815, when the Apothecaries Act originated'. Such a measure may be viewed as perverse but Coley, as ever, had his reasons. Both his immediate relatives, James Coley (his 17-year-old son by his first wife Bertha Davenport) and John Coley Junior (his nephew) held the qualification of LSA. They were therefore, by implication, excluded from applying for a position, as Coley made clear when stating that 'I have been influenced by no sinister motive, having neither filiism nor nepotism in view'. With such a delicate matter resolved in theory it was also stated that any house apothecary appointed to the infirmary would not be allowed to engage in private practice, thus protecting the interests of the local medical men. The apothecary, Coley suggested, would receive a sum of £60 annually, out of which he was expected to provide his own board. Alternatively, any house-surgeon (a rank above that of house apothecary) was to provide his services free of charge, which implied that the post itself would offer prestige and therefore an opportunity to develop a private practice.

But how many people within the community, apart from the gentry, were wealthy enough to engage a doctor when fees, according to Coley, could be as much as £70 for attendance at an accident? Two indicators that may be considered are the 'tenpound householder' survey of 1831, and the Index of Voters for 1832.

The household survey of 1831 was undertaken throughout the Borough of Bridgnorth (which included four adjoining parishes) to ascertain who was eligible to vote under the pending Reform Act of 1832. The Act sought to modernise the political system by extending the vote to householders whose rent was £10 or more: the 'tenpound householder'. From the survey report,[24] the number of qualifying tenements was given as 339, whilst the Index of Voters for 1832[25] – those actually eligible to vote – amounted to 113 householders within the newly proposed boundary, which included 6,171 souls (Table 1).

Table 1. Bridgnorth Borough by Parish

Parish	Tenpound Householder, 1831 [A]	Voters, 1832 [B]
St Leonard	156	43
St Mary Magdalene	114	39
Quatford	23	2
Oldbury	11	8
Tasley	10	3
Astley Abbotts	25	18
TOTAL	339	113

Sources: A: SA 3214/1 Report on the Borough of Bridgnorth.
   B: SA Class q C55.7 The Register of Voters (Southern Division).

The survey report of 1831 also identified that the town possessed 'two or three manu-factories' (one of which was the Southwell carpet works) and that 'a large portion of the labouring class obtained employment in the navigation of the Severn (which, however, was in steep decline with subsequent unemployment).[26] However, the survey report also identified that it was 'the market and retail trade with the neighbourhood' that was 'the principal source of profit to the inhabitants'. But one wonders how much trade there was to be had in Bridgnorth as trade in Shrewsbury, the county town, at the time of William Cobbett's visit in 1830, was, 'on the decline ... The tradesmen were all complaining, because they were not selling half of what they did four or five years before; the ironmongers not a quarter'.[27] With a fragile economy largely dependent upon carpet manufacturing, few gentry and a small number of tenpound household-ers within the Borough, one can only presume that fee-paying patients were few and that a competitive market place existed where inter-professional rivalry for custom must have been rife!

Coley, who appears to have been an ambitious medical man and the driving force behind the infirmary project, certainly engendered a degree of animosity amongst some of those associated with the Dispensary, including Bridgnorth's medical men. As previously mentioned, Coley had been approached by the Dispensary's treasurer 'respecting some practical improvements' at the Dispensary. This was in 1832, but three years later, in 1835, some members of the Dispensary Committee had approached Coley again with a request that he now attend the patients at the Dispensary. He was willing to accept this request, but only with the approval of the Infirmary Committee, and this was subsequently given on 23 December 1835 when it was resolved:

> That, Mr. J.M. Coley having been requested to attend the Patients of the Dispensary
> by the Rev. W. Vickers and others, and Mr Coley having offered to give to the
> Infirmary the profits of his Attendance on such Patients, should he be appointed; it is
> the wish of this meeting that Mr Coley do offer his Services to that Institution.[28]

That same day Coley wrote to Mr Deeton, treasurer of the Dispensary Committee, formally offering his services:[29]

> Dear Sir,
>   Having been particularly requested to attend the patients of the
> Dispensary in this Town, I beg to offer my Services, as one of the
> Surgeons to that Institution.
>   I am, dear Sir,
>   Y[ou]rs Sincerely
>   J.M. Coley
>
> December 23. 1835   Signed: J.[?]. Williams
> To: J. Deeton, Esq   Chairman

On the following day, Thursday 24 December, Mr John Lewis, who appears to have acted as an arbitrator, attended a meeting of the Subscribers to the Dispensary in the Town Hall. In the Chair was W. Wolryche Whitmore Esq. who had succeeded his cousin, Thomas Whitmore, as President of the Dispensary. There were also eight others in attendance, including a Mr Duppa who we will meet again. From John Lewis's report of that meeting we learn of the proceedings,[30] during which a discussion took place on the proposed role of Coley as Surgeon to the Dispensary. It emerged that in the previous year of 1834 the subject of the Infirmary had been contemplated. Considered as an 'impracticable project', the concession had been made that should the Infirmary be accomplished then subscriptions to the Dispensary would, as a matter of course, be transferred to the new medical charity; a concession that did not take effect as those concerned with the Dispensary subsequently chose to remain independent of the new development. Someone at the meeting also 'observed that he did not see why they needed to go into that subject' of the Infirmary, to which Lewis, a supporter of the Infirmary project, responded with his concern 'that the poor should have the best medical advice'. He also fervently hoped that the two institutions would become one – which they would not for a further 35 years! It was also Lewis who had 'urged Mr Coley to allow me to propose him to be one of the Surgeons to the Dispensary' as he had hoped that such a proposition would be 'taken as an offer of conciliation'. But someone else then observed that if Mr Coley accepted the position, 'it would not be worth the while of the other Surgeons to continue their services'. Others had objections and the majority present decided they 'were not to have him'. Whereupon Lewis withdrew his proposal and the matter was dropped.

Perhaps the Surgeons to the Dispensary in 1835 – Messrs Joseph Hall, William Thursfield (Senior), John Williams, Henry Seymour and John Coley Junior – gave a sigh of relief. What surely mattered to Coley was that at the inaugural meeting of the Infirmary in 1832 five resolutions were unanimously adopted: that an infirmary should be built for the labouring population and the poor; that donations in aid of the erection and furnishing of the infirmary be sought and banked at one of four banks, two in Bridgnorth and two in London; that a committee of 'Gentlemen' be constituted to solicit donations and subscriptions in preparation for a General Meeting of the Subscribers at which a Committee of Management would be appointed to execute the business associated with the building and erection of an infirmary; that those who donated £25 or more be considered a Trustee, and every Annual Subscriber of two guineas (£2.2s) or more be a Governor and eligible as a future Committee member and finally, that J.H. Cooper Esq. be appointed Treasurer and that J.M. Coley Esq. be appointed Honorary Secretary.[31]

As for the friction that existed between Coley and his detractors at the Dispensary, the way was now made clear: his services were not required. He could now concentrate, as he had with others of like mind in November 1832, on bringing to fruition the building of an infirmary.

There was much work to be done.

2   A GOAL ACHIEVED

*Small hospitals are in reality more conducive to the cause of science, and better
adapted for the poor to receive the individual attention of the medical officers.*

James Milman Coley, 2 October 1835

WITH the acceptance in November 1832 that plans for an infirmary should
proceed, the year of 1833 proved to be a busy one.[1] Meetings took place at
Coley's house in Mill Street where, on 25 January 1833, Coley introduced Mr James
F. Williams of Oldbury House to the committee members. Williams, who would
replace Mr Cooper as treasurer in the following year, would remain in that honorary
post until 1838 when his circumstances would change. Then, on 27 June (with a building fund established), it was agreed that all donations, paid to the treasurer, should
be transferred immediately into the town's Savings Bank in the names of the Right
Honourable Thomas Whitmore Esq., the Reverend J. [?T] Rowley and Mr J.M.
Coley as 'Trustees for that purpose'. In the following month of July, the subscribers
to the local Board of Health fund also met to authorise the payment of 'about £53' to
Coley, as a donation towards the 'projected Infirmary'.[2]

By August things were moving apace as Mr Josiah Griffiths, the architect-
builder, accompanied by Coley and three committee members met Mr Whitmore,
'by his appointment near the High Rock for the purpose of fixing upon a site for the
Building of the Infirmary'. This meeting ultimately created difficulties and delays
as Mr Whitmore 'objected to the situation'. He therefore proposed to Coley that he
would let a house, currently under loan, at a low rent that could be used as a hospital. Such a scheme was not unusual; indeed, Stevenson has identified that the Salop
Infirmary was still in adapted houses by 1750.[3] However, it was not until April of the
following year, 1834, that Whitmore 'recollected that he had promised the occupation of the House to Mr Charles Clarke'. At some time (the date is not recorded)

Whitmore suggested a new build: it was a proposition to which all concerned were 'urged to secrecy'.

The delays, which 'suspended all further progress' for nearly fourteen months, now saw members absenting themselves from committee meetings whilst others 'abandoned fidelity and support'. To ascertain what support did remain for the project, Coley wrote a circular to all members with the exception of those who were demonstrably active in the scheme:

> *Dear Sir,*
>
> *As it will be necessary to appoint a new Committee for the Bridgnorth Infirmary, every member of which will be required to take an active part in the proceedings; I will thank you to inform me whether your engagements will allow, or your situation dispose you to co-operate with zeal* [and] *energy in completing the undertaking.*
>
> *I am, dear Sir,*   *Bridgnorth*
> *Yours sincerely J.M. Coley*   *Oct. 10, 1834*

With immediate responses from six worthy townsmen, including Joshua Sing, a prominent tanner (as his ancestors had been since the seventeenth century), and the solicitor, Arndell Francis Sparkes to be committee members, a meeting of the new committee took place on 7 November 1834. Added to this group were the previously mentioned Mr John Lewis, a wine merchant and insurance agent of High Town, and Mr Duppa, more properly addressed as Thomas Duppa Esq. As a member of the local gentry, with an estate in Eardington, some two miles south of Bridgnorth, and a second residence in Mill Street, Duppa, in Coley's estimation, became a 'true friend to the cause', for it appears that, after searching, he had found a plot of land belonging to Mr Whitmore. The committee therefore unanimously agreed that Coley should approach Thomas Whitmore 'for such part of a large garden in the New Town, occupied by Mr Lucas, Tanner, as may be found requisite for the erection and build of the Bridgnorth Infirmary'. On 10 November 1834 Coley duly forwarded a letter to Thomas Whitmore in which he stated that:

> *The land has been completely examined by the Committee and appraised of, as eligibly situated with respect to aspect, elevation and a supply both of Severn and pump-water* [spring water], *both of which may be obtained at a trifling expense. It is also in the liberties, remote from any building, retired and at the same time so central that the House–Apothecary and other medical officers will be able to discharge their duties to the resident poor in the Town without inconvenience. Mr Lucas, your tenant, who has been spoken to on this subject by Mr Duppa, is*

willing to give up any part of the Garden, which you may devise to dispose of for
such a charitable purpose.[4]

Coley then hoped that Whitmore would 'not deny the favour', as he considered the situation was 'now urgent' – especially as an institution would 'afford relief to thousands of the poorer classes'. He concluded by reminding Whitmore, in a polite tone, that the 'master Plan, Elevation, Specification and Estimate of the Infirmary, which was prepared by Mr Griffiths [were] left by me at Apley last year' (i.e. 1833; of these documents there is now no trace).

That very day Coley received a reply:

Apley Park,
Mon. Nov. 10, 1834

Dear Sir,

Mr Branson shall call upon you in a day or two and view the spot of Land
you mention, and when he has made his report to me, you shall hear further from me
on the subject.

I remain,
dear Sir,
Yours very Truly
Thomas Whitmore

To J.M. Coley, Esq.

The following day Mr Whitmore's agent, Thomas Branson of Norton, met Messrs Duppa and Williams to examine the garden in New Town, where an agreement was reached on an area of land between Listley Street and Holly Bush Road that 'would ensure the purpose for the infirmary'. It was also agreed that an opening could be made through the Town Wall – a mediaeval boundary wall in Listley Street – through which patients and visitors might access the infirmary, via steps, 'should they dain to pass that way'. A few days later Whitmore received his agent's report and, having spoken to Coley on 24 November, agreed that the portion of land would be made over to the Infirmary's Trustees through a Deed of Gift (this was eventually prepared by Pritchard and Sons, solicitors of Bridgnorth).

There then appears to have been a lull in activity, which may have been related to the committee's lack of success in obtaining sufficient 'donations to [the] Building and Furnishing Fund to the full amount anticipated'. At this date, 11 December 1834, it was also minuted that there was 'difficulty in originating an institution'. Was this a euphemism for the lack of the desired 2,000 guineas to build the proposed Infirmary?

or, perhaps, antipathy towards Coley by some in the community who saw little need for such an establishment? Whatever the reason, the Infirmary Committee resolved to publish a circular, directed at subscribers, and to place an advertisement in the two Shrewsbury newspapers seeking donations from all 'Noblemen and Gentlemen in the County' (the monetary contributions to be lodged with the Bridgnorth bankers, Messrs Coopers and Purton).

Determined to press ahead, the Committee took the next step of marking out the land in New Town. This was undertaken on 18 December, when Messrs Duppa, Williams and Coley met with Whitmore's agent, Mr Branson. Two months later, on 13 February 1835, Coley received a letter from Mr Branson confirming that the land measurements were 'about one rood, six perches statute measure' (just over one quarter of an acre) and that the tenant, Mr Lucas, had 'consented to relinquish any claim he may have upon the ground in question'. The very next day, Coley wrote to Mr Pritchard, solicitor, requesting that he prepare the Deed of Gift on behalf of the Infirmary Committee, whilst informing him that:

> In the Statutes of the government of the Infirmary, it is stated that the Infirmary will be established for the MEDICAL & SURGICAL relief of the labouring and parochial poor in general and of such Servants & other persons as may be in need of its assistance.

The land in New Town, known as Tenter Garden, was previously described as Tainter Hill. This is an apt description for this area of steeply sloping land, which had been associated, since the eighteenth century, with the weaving industry,[5] when a 'tenter', a wooden frame, would have been used to stretch woollen or linen cloth after milling, to prevent it from shrinking. The area of surveyed land with its boundaries and measurements was given in the minutes as:

> N = Listlie [Listley] Street; S = Road leading through the New Town [Holly Bush Road]; E = by Mr Watts Garden etc.; W = by remaining portion of land, called Tenter Garden now in occupation by Mr. Lucas, Tanner, in Bridgnorth ... Length 56 yards from Listlie Street to New Town Road; Breadth 30 yards at the top, adjoining Listlie Street and 21 yards breadth at bottom adjoining New Town Road.[6]

By 3 April 1835, Mr Griffiths had provided an estimate of £25 12s 'for the erection of a wall to fence the boundary of the Infirmary Land towards Mr Lucas's garden', and three days later he proceeded to build the wall, having been given permission by Coley. Four months later, on 21 August, a combined committee and subscribers' meeting took place at Mr Coley's house, at which Mr Griffiths' proposed plan for the Infirmary and his estimate of £840 for the build was discussed. As no adverse comments were minuted it is presumed that both the estimate and the plan, which must have been modified to meet the disappointing sum raised, were approved. On 17 September the committee requested that Mr Vickers, solicitor, immediately prepare a 'Copy of the Agreement' with Mr Griffiths for signature, thus formalising the arrangement with him and enabling the building works to commence.

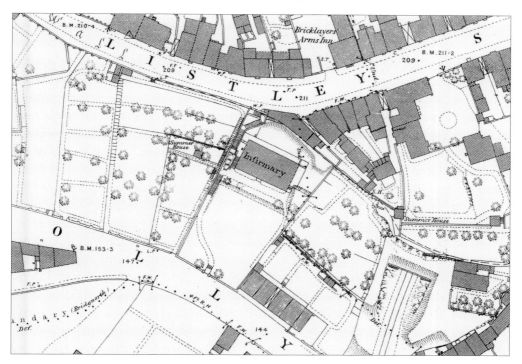

An Ordnance Survey map showing the site of the original Bridgnorth Infirmary located between Listley Street (N) and Holly Bush Road (S) on land gifted to the trustees of the Infirmary by Thomas Whitmore of Apley Park in 1835. © Crown Copyright 1884

Attention now turned to the stone-laying ceremony and the invitation of dignitaries, amongst whom would be the Honourable R.H. Clive, MP who would lay the first stone of the Bridgnorth Infirmary. In the interim, Dr Jonas Malden, MD, a consultant physician to the Worcester Infirmary, had offered his services to the Bridgnorth Infirmary. This physician, whose offer was formally accepted by the committee on 4 November 1835, was an elderly gentleman who, in 1818, was appointed as a consultant after 40 years' service at Worcester[7] (this suggests he was lending his name rather than his clinical services to Bridgnorth's new infirmary!)

In *Watton's Cuttings*[8] a newspaper report offers a glimpse of the stone-laying ceremony that took place on Friday 2 October 1835. At an early hour, flags were hung and a temporary covering and seats 'for the company' were erected in the Infirmary's grounds. Later that morning a gathering of the great and the good met at Mr Coley's house in Low Town from whence they processed to the site in High Town. Arriving at twelve o'clock to the ringing of bells, 'a large concourse of people had already stationed themselves to witness the interesting scene', which the correspondent, Old Subscriber, described as consisting 'of the very lowest classes, aided by the charity children who had made it their playground'. He also noted that there was an 'entire absence of all the medical men, with one exception; a circumstance that called forth many enquiries'.[9]

Mr Coley then 'opened the business' and, in a long address, spoke of the 'numerous obstacles, arising from ignorance, prejudice, and design [that] soon presented themselves, as generally happens in attempts to establish a medical charity'. To those who had deserted the cause he trusted 'that the hearts of many of them are now with us.' In a solicitous tone he then praised Mr Thomas Charlton Whitmore, MP and son of Thomas Whitmore, for his 'fidelity and attachment' to the cause. Praise was also given to the treasurer, Mr J.F. Williams, for the 'glorious victory of this day accomplished.' Nor was Mr Duppa forgotten, for it was his 'judicious selection of the ground, on which our institution is being erected' that was due solely to him.

Although the primary motive for establishing the Infirmary had been the inadequacy of the dispensary in serving the needs of the sick poor, Coley's motives were more complex and associated with wider issues, as can be seen from the extract below:

> When I first projected the establishment of an Infirmary, connected with an extensive Dispensary, I was chiefly intent on destroying the vicious system of farming out the parochial poor by means of medical contracts. The moral happiness of the poor is in great measure dependent on their health, and, when diseases or accidents are judiciously treated in the first instance, much subsequent misery and parochial expenditure are avoided. Unfortunately the Commissioners, acting under the Poor Laws [sic] Amendment Bill, have aggravated the evils of which I complain, by encouraging contracts which have a still more direct tendency to injure the interests of and degrade the character of the medical profession. Hence petitions, signed by the medical men in the different counties of England, have been presented to Parliament loudly complaining of the oppressive effects of the Act in question.[10]

The implementation of the 1834 Act saw the imposition of contractual employment placed upon medical men through local Poor Law Guardians, who put work in the public medical services out to tender. The Guardians, who hired and fired medical men, sought the lowest tender. This saved money on the local Poor Rates (a tax) for a contract (known as a 'Parish Contract') that was part-time and for which remuneration was pitifully small for an onerous workload. The Hon. Clive, MP had been 'connected' with the Medical Committee in the House of Commons, and was thus acquainted with the grievances of medical men in relation to these 'Parish Contracts'. According to Coley, both he and Mr Clive believed that:

> *no medical institution can be well conducted unless the moral principles of the poor are duly cultivated and brought into co-operation with the bounty of the rich and the gratuitous services of well-educated medical practitioners.*

It was a principle upon which the Infirmary was to be founded, where humanitarianism supported by the wealthy and the free services of medical practitioners combined to form a 'system of social relationships of the day' that was characteristic of the early Victorian medical services.[11]

Coley went on to support his argument for the building of a 'small infirmary' which he considered more 'conducive to the cause of science, and better adapted for the poor to receive the undivided attention of the medical officers'. However, it appears there was an issue over bed numbers – 24 to 30 beds were projected in 1832 – as Coley speaks of the eminent surgeon 'Sir Astley Cooper, London [who] attended an [*sic*] hospital containing only 15 beds'. German hospitals, he added, averaged 15–25 beds. As Richardson states: 'The ideal number of beds was a point of argument, but in general half a dozen beds was considered ample in agricultural areas'.[12] From a Report of the House Committee in 1885,[13] when the state of the Infirmary required the closure of wards for refurbishment, it appears that three wards existed, and not six as originally envisaged. Two wards each contained three beds, whilst the third, a 'small ward', contained an unrecorded number of beds. However, *Kelly's Directory* of 1885 reported that the Infirmary contained eight beds, in which case the 'small ward' contained two beds.

Coley continued with his address, and spoke of Dr Malden, the 'Physician of eminence at Worcester, who has generously thrown the mantle of science over our infant institution'. Physicians, unlike surgeons and apothecaries, tended to be university educated and therefore were deemed, by themselves and others, to be at the top of the medical hierarchy. Such a professional connection, according to Coley in a flight of fancy, would therefore 'render' the Infirmary 'accessible to patients recommended from any part of the kingdom'. Coley also reminded those present that the benefits of the charity were to be limited to the town and neighbourhood, and that the charity itself was to be self-supporting. Income was to be derived in part from so-called 'free' subscribers (the hard working 'deserving poor') each of whom, according to the Infirmary's 1837 AGM report made a financial contribution of five shillings each per annum. Alternatively, 'annual honorary subscribers' (the bourgeois and aristocracy, which included the Earls of Darlington, Liverpool and Stamford & Warrington) were expected to provide an annual contribution of one guinea or more. In concluding his oration Coley also stated that the last 'two to three years' had incurred a 'great sacrifice of time and interruptions to my studies and domestic comfort ... in hastening the progress of this good work'. This may have been a reference to his publishing activities in the various medical journals of the day, including the *Lancet*.[14]

Attention now turned to the laying of the foundation stone, under which Mr Clive had deposited a silver coin of the present King (William IV, 1830–1837). Once the foundation stone had been laid, three large cheers ensued 'as a signal for the discharge of cannon, planted on the opposite hill, across the valley' (an area which is now a housing estate known as 'The Hawthorns'). Mr Clive then proceeded to address the company, during which he declared that the inhabitants of Bridgnorth were 'favoured' by a 'competent number of medical practitioners', whilst acknowledging that the 'poorer classes' could not afford the attentions of medical men 'as we can do'. Turning next to address 'the Poor', in a paternalist tone redolent of the period, he reminded them that:

> *when a cure or relief has been afforded, you must not forget to feel grateful; and should any of you pay the debt of nature while in this establishment* [mortality rates in hospitals were high], *your friends must feel satisfied that you have received every advantage which the greatest skill and the best human means can afford.*[15]

He concluded by congratulating those concerned on obtaining the services of Dr Malden, and hoped that the Bridgnorth Infirmary would flourish whilst simultaneously 'disseminating health and vigour to every object of charity in the neighbourhood'. The proceedings then closed and the 'large party' returned to Mr Coley's house where they 'sat down at a collation'. After the meal, Coley presented 'the Silver Trowel inclosed [*sic*] in a redwood box, lined with satin, to the Hon. R.H. Clive'. The inscription on the upper surface of the trowel read:

The First Stone of the
BRIDGNORTH INFIRMARY
Laid by the Hon. R.H. Clive, M.P.
October 2, 1835
"And all that see it shall say this hath God done; for
they shall perceive that it is his work."
PSALM lxiv, VERSE 9.

On the reverse was inscribed:

"Presented by J.M. Coley, M.R.C.S.L. &c. &c.
The Founder of the Institution".

It was the end of what must have been a momentous day, for the principal actors had achieved, against considerable opposition, their goal: the establishing of the Bridgnorth Infirmary. However, the treasurer's work was not yet finished, for on that same day Mr J.F. Williams listed the 'Expenses incurred in laying the first stone of the Infirmary'[16] as:

	£	s	d
Ringers	2	0	0
Mr Griffiths for his workmen	2	0	0
John Higgs for the use of his guns		5	0
Gunpowder and wadding		7	4
Thomason for colours [flags]		5	0
D[itt]o himself and father		7	0
Mr Lewis conveying Benches to ground		1	0

There was now a need to consider the appointment of one house-apothecary and two annually elected surgeons, in addition to James Milman Coley as Surgeon for Life. The decision was therefore taken to place an advertisement in both the *Salopian Journal* and the *Wolverhampton Chronicle* (to no effect) whilst Bridgnorth's medical men – Messrs Joseph Hall, George Davis, John Williams, William Proud, Henry Seymour, William Thursfield (Senior), Edward Parry, J.N. Heathcote and surprisingly, John Coley, Junior – were sent a circular,[17] forwarded through the Post Office, which read:

Sir,

By direction of the Trustees of the Bridgnorth Infirmary, I beg to inform you that, preparatory to the election of two Surgeons to that Institution, Candidates are required to forward their Testimonials of Surgical Qualifications, under Seal, to me, for inspection of the Trustees, on or before Monday, December 7; and Candidates for the Office of House Apothecary are also requested to send their Testimonials as above directed.

I am, Sir,
Your obedient Servant,
J.M. Coley,
Secretary.

November 30, 1835.
Bridgnorth.

Perhaps it was the tone of the letter, or the need to possess a surgical qualification, or the antipathy towards Coley following his scathing comments about his colleagues as 'Parish doctors' that made it impossible for Bridgnorth's medical men to respond to the circular. Whatever the reason, there was an unwillingness on the part of these medical men to be involved with the new infirmary, as none came forward to support an institution that would soon open its doors to the 'deserving poor'.

With the year of 1835 coming to a close Mr Griffiths, the architect-builder, was paid the sum of £292 on 30 November, which was complemented by a further payment of £128 on 5 December. This made a total of £420, representing 50 per cent of the approved estimate of £840 for the design and build of the Infirmary. On Christmas Eve, 24 December 1835, the building was presumably nearing completion, as against a Mr Edward Curtis's name there is the payment of a 'Premium for effecting insurance of £500 on the building from 28 November 1835 to 24 December 1836'.

With such speedy progress, two other important matters required attention – particularly as the Infirmary was to open its doors to the sick poor in the first days of February 1836.[18] The first was the 'intended footway' from Listley Street, down the hillside to the Infirmary, which necessitated an opening through the Town Walls. The decision to proceed with the works, taken on 31 December 1835, would include the erection of a series of steep brick steps, iron handrails and a doorway with door that adjoined 'a small House' in Listley Street. The work, which would be undertaken by Mr Griffiths at an estimated cost of £27, would also include extending the wall and roof of the adjoining tenement in March 1836 to prevent fumes from the Infirmary's 'Bath Boiler' chimney annoying the inhabitants of Listley Street.

The second important matter was the lack of a water supply to the Infirmary, which was deemed 'necessary' at a meeting of the Infirmary Committee, in their new Board Room, on 4 February 1836. However, authorisation for the laying down of a water pipe rested with the Bridgnorth Borough Council, now reformed under the Municipal Corporations Act 1835 and led by the Whigs, who resolved on 17 June that a branch pipe could be laid to accommodate the needs of the Infirmary. In 1829 an underground reservoir had been built in the High Street at the south end of the Town Hall.[19] A branch pipe from the reservoir to the National School (erected 1820) in Listley Street had already been laid, thus enabling another branch from this pipe to be laid to a water conduit that would service the Infirmary from 1836. The site of the water conduit still exists, but not the water conduit of c.1871[20] (which presumably replaced the 1836 model) as it was removed in 2001; its subsequent fate unknown.

As for the untreated water, this was originally to be free of annual payments; however, the Water Committee chose to levy a charge. From the Infirmary's 1837 statement of expenditure[21] a sum of £1 was paid for 'Water Rent, five quarters', which suggests that the water supply to the conduit existed from about October 1836. There was, of course, no internal supply of water at the Infirmary (and therefore no water closets). What water was needed had to be fetched and carried, via the steep steps, from the water conduit on Listley Street. In this same year of 1836 the items, 'Snuffers and Tray', were also purchased, which implies that candles were used to provide artificial light, whilst other light would have been provided by firelight and daylight.

In the six months that had elapsed between the Infirmary's opening in February and 3 August 1836, the Trustees reported that:

> *589 patients have been admitted, of which number 204 have been discharged cured – seven have died – and the remainder, exclusive of 150 now under treatment, have received relief.*[22]

The report, published in three provincial newspapers, included a plea to the wider public for funds to enable the purchase of 'an adequate stock of beds and other articles of furniture'. The report also identified that 'many accidents' had been brought to the Infirmary and that the lack of beds had resulted in a 'limited' number of operations being performed. The causes of the 'many accidents' are not identified, but at this time mechanised farming, with such agricultural tools as mechanical threshers and iron-framed ploughs, was becoming commonplace in agricultural communities such as Bridgnorth.[23]

This same report also stated that 79 children had been vaccinated, free of charge, by the 'House Surgeon' (which may have been a reference to the house-apothecary appointed in January 1836). The condition being combated through a government policy initiative was smallpox, an endemic infectious disease of deadly proportions that was prevalent, but not exclusively, among children. It was an initiative that, by 1871, culminated in what has been termed the 'Victorian Health Service'.[24]

In the meantime, the official post of Matron was established at the Infirmary with the appointment of a Mrs Collins in June 1836, whilst the two posts of annually elected surgeons remained unfilled (leaving Coley with an onerous workload in addition to his private practice). To ameliorate this burdensome problem Coley decided, in 1837, to engage a partner to assist him in his various duties. Whether this appointment was made in haste is unknown, but it was a decision that Coley would come to regret.

The year of 1837 also saw the management and business of the Infirmary regularised. The officers of the charity were reappointed and gave themselves the power to add to their number. Other deliberations included those articles relating to medical men and their eligibility to practice, which were rescinded and amended to read:

> **Article No.22** That no Surgeon be eligible to officiate in this Institution, unless he lives in Bridgnorth and be a Member of the Royal College of Surgeons in London, Dublin, Edinburgh or Faculty of Glasgow, or have been

practicing his Profession in Bridgnorth before the Year 1836 and can attest Surgical Testimonies satisfactory to the majority of the Trustees.

Article No.24 That no House-Apothecary be eligible to the office of Surgeon to this Institution, unless he have [*sic*] officiated as Apothecary to it during three years and be a Member of one of the before mentioned Colleges of Surgeons.[25]

The latter part of 1837 also found Coley working at the Infirmary assisted by his young medical partner (now designated as an 'annual' elected surgeon following an alteration to a rule) and a resident house-apothecary, neither of whom had any apparent affiliation with either Bridgnorth's medical men or the dispensary. Patient numbers at the latter had slowly dwindled from 314 in 1835 to 273 in 1840.[26] By contrast, the Infirmary's 1837 annual report identified their out-patient numbers as being 1,805 at the end of that year.[27]

Such success in meeting the needs of the independent sick poor – if numbers are considered as an indicator – was marred when the accusation was made by an unnamed person that medicines had been sold at the Infirmary. The charge, which was investigated and found to be 'utterly unfounded', was also perceived as being 'injurious to the character of the [Infirmary's] officers'. It was an incident that would soon pale into insignificance, for in 1838 a series of disputes commenced that resulted in significant changes for both individuals and the Infirmary, as the viability of the Infirmary as a medical charity came into question.

3   DISSENSION AT THE INFIRMARY

The Committee are sorry to be obliged to report that the benefits of the Institution have been somewhat curtailed during the past year, in consequence of the unfortunate disagreement which took place between them and the late Senior Surgeon, and which rendered his removal from his office absolutely necessary.

The Fourth Annual Report of the Bridgnorth Infirmary, 1839

APPOINTED on 29 January 1836 as the Infirmary's first resident house-apothecary was Mr John Phillips, LSA, MRCS. Born in the village of Astley Abbotts, this 25-year-old medical man was duly rewarded for his exertions as he was re-elected, on an annual basis, until 1839 when he was appointed as an honorary surgeon to the institution. It was a position that he would hold until 1862 when he was first recorded as an honorary consulting surgeon; a post that he retained until his death in 1868 having served the Infirmary for 32 years.

Such longevity of service suggests that Mr Phillips was perceived as a valued medical practitioner: indeed in 1837, following the enquiry of the sale of medicines, it was noted that thanks were due to him for his 'valuable services'. He also appears to have been a medical man who was willing to abide by all the numerous rules of the Infirmary, and distance himself from others in times of conflict. Certainly during the years of 1838 to 1840, when deep divisions occurred between James Milman Coley and others, Mr Phillips' name is distinguished by its absence from the minutes.

The same cannot be said of James Milman Coley (1784–1867) whose medical education was nurtured by his father, William Coley (1756–1841). A native of Tewkesbury, William came to Bridgnorth in 1779, having completed a seven-year apprenticeship under the tutelage of a Mr B. Tipton, 'Apothecary to the Worcester Infirmary'. Commencing business in Low Town as a 'Surgeon and Apothecary', William soon found himself a wife from the nearby hamlet of Bromley by the name of Elizabeth

Smithyman whom he married on 17 December 1780 at Worfield Church.[1] Aged 24, this apparently ambitious young medical man, in seeking to establish his medical credentials, also had his name inserted in the *Medical Directory* of 1780. Five years later an article, written by William, appeared in the *Gentleman's Magazine* in which he described 'a form of ague' and its treatment, which was then prevalent in the town of Bridgnorth.[2] Established as a resident of the town, on 18 February 1789 William Coley was elected as a Burgess (or freeman) of the Borough of Bridgnorth: 'the expence [sic] of w[hi]ch cost £3 8s od'.[3] He would also serve as a bailiff (or court official) in the years of 1804, 1815 and 1821[4] by which time Elizabeth had borne William eight children.

Their first born, John, was variously described as a veterinary surgeon and later as a druggist and grocer; whilst their third born, James Milman, would become a surgeon and physician. Both sons, including the son of John, John Coley, Junior, LSA – who was apprenticed to his grandfather[5] – would all become Burgesses of the Borough of Bridgnorth[6] during their respective lifetimes.

But what of James Milman Coley, who appears to have been a 'chip off the old block'? In the absence of any records it is assumed that James Milman was apprenticed to his father and that William's medical practice was successful, as James Milman was to further his medical education in London where indenture fees to a hospital surgeon were high.[7] He attended St Bartholomew's Hospital where James Milman studied under the eminent John Abernethy (1764–1831)[8] who sought to 'turn surgery from craft into science'.[9] In seeking out such an illustrious tutor, James Milman must have been an ambitious young man with an enquiring mind; his father must also have considered his son worthy of the expenditure! Gaining membership of the Royal College of Surgeons (London) during 1806, the 22-year-old James Milman returned to Bridgnorth where, on 18 August 1807, he too was enrolled as a Burgess of the Borough of Bridgnorth. He had also joined his father's medical practice; an arrangement that was formalised by a partnership that would not be dissolved until 1830,[10] by which time James Milman had consolidated his position as a general practitioner and surgeon in the town.

The year of 1830 also witnessed the death of George IV, prompting a general election that brought the Whigs to power, whose many reforms would alter the social, economic and moral fabric of the country over the ensuing years.[11] Support for the Whigs was drawn from a nascent middle class that in Bridgnorth included Nonconformists, the three leading carpet manufacturers – the McMichaels, Griersons and Southwells – and the Quatford architect, John Smalman.[12] There were others that would come to include James Milman Coley, whose political leanings at this time rested with the local Tories[13] who would later re-brand themselves as Conservatives.

One of the many Whig policies that would have societal repercussions was the introduction of the Reform Act of 1832 which, as previously mentioned, broadened the franchise. This right to vote would also be extended with the introduction of the Municipal

Corporation Act of 1835 that brought radical change to local government. Out went Bridgnorth's self-perpetuating system that favoured the few and in came a uniform system and the division of the town into four wards: East, West, Castle and Morfe. As a reformed Municipal Borough, a Mayor, four aldermen and twelve councillors would be elected annually by the ratepayers to oversee the town's affairs, whilst the appointed posts of town clerk[14] and treasurer were to be salaried and independent of the Borough Council.[15] Such reform found the Whigs, who increasingly were known as Liberals, entering office where they were represented in Bridgnorth by the previously mentioned Joshua Sing, a Baptist tanner and active supporter of the Infirmary. As the town's first elected mayor, Joshua Sing was supported by 'its newly elected Whig council' whose members held their first meeting on New Year's Day, 1836.[16]

Amongst the council members there was another supporter of the Infirmary, namely James Shipley (or Shepley) RN who, on 9 November 1836, was elected Mayor of Bridgnorth. Described variously as 'a Whig [who was] unfortunately a violent political partisan' and 'a strong Liberal',[17] Shipley had the misfortune to preside over a riotous parliamentary election in July 1837. He eventually declared Messrs Thomas Charlton Whitmore (Tory) and Henry Hanbury-Tracy (Whig) duly elected; the latter by four votes.[18] The outcome was successfully challenged by the other Tory candidate, Robert Pigot, in consequence of Mayor Shipley 'closing the poll before the proper time'.[19] This resulted in Hanbury-Tracy accepting the Chiltern Hundreds, thus enabling him to resign from the House of Commons. As for Shipley, it is said that he 'lost many friends among the Conservative party'[20] including, it would seem, those clergymen who sat with Shipley on the Infirmary committee, as several days later a minute declares that Shipley's name is to be 'erased' from the committee.[21] No explanation is given for this decision, leaving one to surmise that Shipley's politics and his actions during the general election were deemed too controversial and divisive for him to remain in Bridgnorth. Hence, perhaps, his swift departure for Cheltenham from where he continued to support the Infirmary as an annual subscriber for a further year.

As for James Milman Coley, there is nothing to indicate how he responded to Shipley's sudden departure from the Infirmary committee. Doubtless he had other matters on his mind as his medical and administrative duties at the institution were impinging upon his private practice. As a consequence, he decided to engage a young man to assist him by the name of James Henry Martin who had received his 'Diploma' of the Royal College of Surgeons of Edinburgh on 1 March 1836.[22] Whether, on moving south, Martin had obtained the necessary licence from the Apothecaries' Company in London is a moot point that Coley would come to question, with good cause!

Meanwhile, Coley and Martin regularised their professional arrangement through 'Articles of Appointment for a Co-Partnership' that were drawn up during 1837. In this same year Coley, with the permission of the Infirmary's trustees, altered a rule that included the word 'Diploma', thereby allowing Martin to become an annual surgeon to the institution; a rule that would come into effect on 5 October 1837. This date also saw the appointment of yet another house-apothecary who, like two previous ones, would resign some six months later, on this occasion to be replaced by a Mr Roycraft (or Roycroft), of whom more later.

And so we come to the year of 1838, a year in which James Milman was 54 years old and the author of numerous medical papers, four of which were published during 1838 in the *Lancet*,[23] a radical medical journal whose founder, the surgeon (and previous pugilist) Thomas Wakley (1795–1862), was not adverse to criticising the medical elite. This body of collegiate gentlemen, who had little desire to reform their respective medical colleges, failed to accommodate the needs of their members who, like Coley, were the rank-and-file of the medical profession. Denied a voice within the medical establishment, local societies were formed, such as the pre-eminent Provincial Medical and Surgical Association (PMSA), the precursor (in 1855) of the British Medical Association.[24] Founded by Dr Charles Hastings (1794–1866) of the Worcester Infirmary – where an educational centre acknowledges his achievements – a local branch of the PMSA was formed at Shrewsbury on 12 June 1838. This was known as the Shropshire and North Wales District Branch, and amongst those attending the inaugural meeting was James Milman Coley who was elected as a founding council member for the Bridgnorth District having previously '… expressed himself with much force on the necessity that existed of maintaining by every means the respectability of the profession … '[25]

Was this reported view, which was 'expressed with much force' on professional 'respectability', indicative of Coley's temperament in which outspokenness rather than considered speech set him apart from others? If so, perhaps it is not surprising that he came into conflict with others at the Infirmary, including his partner, James Henry Martin. But as Coley would discover, there were those at the Infirmary who had an alternative agenda and some, like Coley, had also been founding members of the Conservative Club that was formed (following the riotous election) to combat the influence of the 'Whig-Radicals' and their supporters in the Borough constituency by promoting the Conservative cause in the name of Queen, God and Country. By October 1838 the club was known as the Bridgnorth Conservative Association and its president was Thomas Whitmore, who was also the president and a trustee of the Infirmary. The vice-president of the Association was J.F. Williams Esq. (whom we will shortly meet, for he was the treasurer to the Infirmary committee). There was also an ordinary member of the Association, James Henry Martin[26] whose appointment as an elected annual surgeon to the Infirmary was originally endorsed by Coley in 1837 but not thereafter as Coley began to question the conduct of his young partner. A further concern for Coley was the demeanour of five, then six, Anglican clergymen (all members of the Infirmary Committee) who united in what Coley would later describe as: 'the violence of party-spirit and the obstinacy of prejudice'[27] in their orchestrated endeavours to remove him from office, and ultimately the Infirmary.

Meanwhile, all seemed relatively calm at the Infirmary. However, on 14 June 1838, at a meeting of the Infirmary committee,[28] the house-apothecary, Mr Roycraft, made a complaint against the treasurer, J.F. Williams, Esq. who, in turn, made a complaint against Coley, as secretary, for refusing to convene a meeting of the Infirmary Committee. As far as Coley was concerned the incident was deemed to be of a personal nature and therefore not within the Rules of the Infirmary. Williams, however, thought otherwise, which led to a committee meeting being held – in Coley's absence – to consider the various grievances. Chaired by the Revd Dr Thomas Rowley, 'a staunch Tory'[29] and headmaster of Bridgnorth Grammar School, the committee expressed 'their strong disapprobation' of Coley's conduct, whilst Roycraft's conduct was considered 'highly disrespectful' as he had absented himself from the meeting. A request was therefore made to Roycraft to attend a special meeting of the committee (at which Coley would be present) on 21 June when his complaint against the treasurer could be investigated.

In the interim James Henry Martin, having celebrated his 23rd birthday on the 14 June, wrote a testimonial six days later in which he repeated a conversation, made by Williams about Roycraft, which was perceived by the house-apothecary as impugning his character.[30] Whether Martin had provided this testimonial of his own accord or at the behest of others on the committee is unknown, but at the special meeting on 21 June the committee found Coley in breach of Rule 19 for failing to hold a meeting at the express wish of the treasurer. They also upheld Roycraft's complaint against the treasurer who, affronted by the decision, resigned his post but not his membership of the committee! Into the vacancy stepped the Revd John Purton of Oldbury Rectory, who would hold the position of treasurer and, at intervals, that of secretary until his death in 1883.

As for the meeting of 21 June, it must have been a stormy one as it was minuted that Coley had inserted a lengthy protest against the proceedings of 14 June: a protest that was to be 'expunged'. There were also copious notes appended to the minutes of 21 June that would not be 'erased' until the following year of 1839. Then, at a further meeting on 3 July Roycraft, for some inexplicable reason, was required to offer an apology to Mr Williams, which he refused to do, preferring instead to offer his resignation, which was accepted on the stipulation that he provide three months' notice from 29 June. Following his departure an advertisement was placed in the *Lancet* and an application form forwarded to the Birmingham School of Medicine for the position of house apothecary that would not be filled for several weeks. And so it had begun: the sorry tale of 'disgraceful proceedings' at the Infirmary.

In the interim, Coley and the young James Henry Martin agreed to undertake the house-apothecary's duties that included attending to 'operative' patients and preparing prescription medicines. By 4 October Martin's work at the Infirmary had obviously met with the approval of the committee, as the minutes record that they had 'confidence in Mr Martin's attention to his patients'. This 'confidence', however, was not shared by Coley; indeed he must have had serious reservations about Martin as Coley chose, having taken legal advice, to terminate their partnership, which was dissolved on 22 October 1838.[31] Arriving three days later to commence his duties as house-apothecary was Mr W.B. Winchester. Little is known of this medical man, other than that he aligned himself with Coley and in so doing a friendship was formed; one that would last over decades, when both had long since departed from the Infirmary and the town of Bridgnorth.[32] Meanwhile Martin, aggrieved by his changed circumstances, proceeded to slander Coley whilst continuing to assert that 'he was qualified to practice as an apothecary [and that he had] a private arrangement between the Society of Apothecaries in London, and the College of Surgeons, in Edinburgh'.[33] Coley, distrustful of such claims, now sought information from an authoritative source by writing to the Society of Apothecaries in London on 20 November 1838:

> *Gentlemen, I will thank you to inform me whether the Society of Apothecaries in London have made any arrangement with the College of Surgeons in Edinburgh, which, in defiance of the Apothecaries' Act entitles the members of the said College to practice as Apothecaries in England and Wales without a licence from the London Apothecaries Company. Such a representation has been made by interested parties with the view of deterring Apothecaries from informing against Scotch surgeons, and prohibiting the latter from practicing as Apothecaries in England without a licence. As no exemption of this kind is to be found in the Act of 1815, it appears unjust towards Licentiates of the London Apothecaries Company that Edinburgh surgeons should be permitted to violate the Act: and I shall feel obliged if you will have the goodness to inform me whether you have discontinued to enforce the penalties incurred by Edinburgh surgeons, as many such, some of whom to my knowledge are incapable of translating an English prescription into Latin, are at this time illegally practicing in England as Apothecaries, to the injury and disadvantage of Licentiates of your own Society.*
>
> *I shall esteem it a favour if you will transmit me such a reply, as you may have no objection for me to publish in the provincial or other newspapers, etc. with the view of correcting the error alluded to, and supporting the interests of a large body of Licentiates of your Company against an illegal encroachment on the part of members of the Edinburgh College of Surgeons.*

I have the honor [sic] *to remain, Gentlemen,*
Your obedient servant,
    J.M. Coley

A reply, written on the 22 November 1838 by R.B. Upton, Clerk to the Society, followed. In a somewhat tired tone he stated:

Sir, in reply to your letter of the 20th instant, I beg to inform you that this Society has not made any arrangement with the College of Surgeons of Edinburgh, which entitles the members of that College to practice as Apothecaries in England: and it must be obvious to you that such an arrangement between the two bodies would be opposed to the provisions of the Act of Parliament for the better regulating the practices of Apothecaries in England and Wales.

Having received his reply, Coley then forwarded copies of the letters to the editor of the *Ten Town's Messenger*, a Kidderminster newspaper, on the 26 November, which were duly published on 7 December.[34]

The desire to be published – and later to be damned in Coley's case – was not unusual in the nineteenth century. Indeed, grievances were often expressed through the medium of the newspaper, as we saw earlier between Old Subscriber and Philantropos. That Coley and others wrote to newspapers outside the town of Bridgnorth is explained by the absence of a publication that would not materialise until 1852 when the *Bridgnorth Beacon* was first published.

As for Coley's concerns over the legitimacy of his partner's qualifications, this too highlights a wider issue that primarily concerned Scottish educated medical men who, upon qualifying, chose to migrate south of the border into England and Wales to practice. In the Scottish universities of Edinburgh and Glasgow, both physicians and surgeons followed the same medical course and after qualifying often acted as general medical practitioners when moving south. It was essential, therefore, that Scottish educated medical men, when moving south, obtain a licence to practice from the Apothecaries Society in London if they wished to avoid prosecution under Section 20 of the 1815 Apothecaries Act.[35]

Why James Milman Coley chose to air his grievances in public, in which he alludes to Martin in all but name, is difficult to comprehend at this distance and without the facts. Tensions between the two obviously existed as yet another private squabble occurred on 1 February 1839 when Martin, in the presence of others, assaulted Coley in the Infirmary premises over a monetary draft that he demanded be made out to him rather than his sister. As Coley later explained, it was Martin's sister who was the rightful recipient, which is why he refused to make the draft out to

Martin. As a result of this fracas, Coley wrote to the trustees in the expectation that they would address Martin's behaviour. He would wait in vain as Martin, knowing of Coley's letter, approached members of the Infirmary committee who subsequently placed a demand upon Coley to convene a special meeting on 4 March so that the difficulties between the two surgeons might be 'investigated'. This special meeting, as with a previous meeting, would proceed without Coley in attendance; it would also be the first of many that would set a pattern for future meetings with, ultimately, serious repercussions for Coley.

From the minute books there is a suggestion of a bias towards Coley, one that was confirmed with the discovery of Coley's *A Faithful Report of the Late Disgraceful Proceedings at the Bridgnorth Infirmary* (hereafter *A Faithful Report*). For within those pages the actions of Martin and the committee members are disclosed – as are their inactions – that reveal the official minutes as being, in today's parlance, economical with the truth.

Why the five clergymen – the Reverends Thomas Rowley, William Knox Marshall, George Bellett, all of Bridgnorth; John Purton of Oldbury and William Moore of Tasley – chose, alongside J.F. Williams Esq. and later, the Reverend Cornelius F. Broadbent of Worfield, to collude with Martin in Coley's downfall is unfathomable. Coley writes of 'party-spirit', but was this partisanship related solely to Bridgnorth's politics? It's a question I leave others to explore, but the founding of voluntary hospitals and infirmaries as charitable institutions was not without hostility during the eighteenth and nineteenth centuries, due to party politics and what has been termed 'political religious' groups all of whom, it would seem, engendered varying degrees of conflict and disharmony during that time.[36]

Certainly all those clergy previously mentioned were either avowed Tories (Rowley and Bellett) or associated with Tories through their family connections (Purton and Broadbent), whilst others presumably knew where their loyalties lay as Knox Marshall, including Bellett, were dependent for their respective livings upon the Whitmores of Apley, and Moore upon a branch of the Acton family and their Tasley Estate. From the Bridgnorth Poll Book[37] all, with the exception of Rowley and Broadbent whose names are absent from the listings, were recorded as having voted for the two Tory candidates, Whitmore and Pigot. Such a revelation is not surprising as at this time: 'there was a long-standing connection between the Church of England and the Tory party, parallel to the Whig connection to dissent'.[38]

Politics aside, let us now return to the special meeting of 4 March 1839 that was initially chaired by Thomas Rowley who, upon being called away, was replaced by William Knox Marshall. Four resolutions were passed in Coley's absence. The first three are given in full to allow an appreciation of their contents:

Resolution 1: That it is the opinion of the Committee that Mr. Coley having acknowledged that certain letters published by him in the *Ten Towns Messenger* of 7th December last had special reference to Mr. Martin one of the Surgeons of the Institution, has thereby rendered himself liable to the penalty provided by the forty third rule.

Resolution 2: That having heard Mr. Coley's statement (read by Mr. Winchester on his behalf) and also Mr. Martin's reply and having seen the Articles of Agreement for a Co-Partnership between Mr. Coley and Mr. Martin they are of [the] opinion that Mr. Martin has not practised any deception towards Mr. Coley, with regard to his medical qualifications or acted in any way dishonestly towards him.

Resolution 3: That with respect to Mr. Martin's conduct on the First of February last, they cannot but express their regret and disapprobation at such proceedings having taken place at the Institution, but considering the Provocation which Mr. Martin had received and the ample apology made by him to the Committee, they do not consider it needful to pass any heavier censure upon him.

Resolution 4 referred to the meeting being adjourned to Tuesday 12 March at noon.[39] A number of points arise from these minutes which led Coley to publish a circular on 22 March in which he seeks to put his interpretation of the events before the public. This questioning of the committee and its version of events will lead, on this and further occasions, to accusations of Coley 'directly impeaching the truth of the committee'. Similarly, Coley's published letter to the Society of Apothecaries and his circular will also, in the eyes of the committee members, render Coley as being 'liable to the penalty provided by the forty third rule': an explanation of which will shortly follow.

Those points that Coley repudiates are first: that the letter to the Society of Apothecaries did not have 'special reference to Mr. Martin' (rather, the letters were published 'for the benefit of the profession'); second, Coley refutes the assertion that the 'Articles of Agreement for a Co-Partnership ...' between him and Martin were seen by the committee, as Coley maintained that the documents had not been out of his possession; third, the committee considered that Martin had 'not practiced any deception towards Mr. Coley with regard to his medical qualification'. However, Coley now knew that Martin did not have the requisite certificate from the Society of Apothecaries to practice in England, which raises the question: was Martin deceiving the members of the committee or were they colluding with him for their own purposes?

Six months later Martin, who had received a 'Letter of Caution' from the Society of Apothecaries, was granted two weeks' leave by the Infirmary Committee so that he might travel to London (with a character reference provided by the Revd Knox Marshall) where he was scheduled to attend Apothecaries Hall on 26 September. Martin failed to attend on that date, but did so a week later when he was approved on 3 October.[40] Fourth, the committee considered that the 'Provocation' Martin had received was due entirely to Coley as he had refused to endorse a draft to Martin who, as previously mentioned, was not the rightful recipient. Nor is there any mention in the minutes of Martin being censured for his inappropriate and unprofessional act of aggression upon a senior colleague that in normal circumstances would have led to Martin's instant dismissal.

Finally, the minutes of 4 March refer to Coley as being 'liable to the penalty provided by the forty third rule'. This rule was originally devised by Coley, as were all the rules of the Infirmary and, subject to scrutiny, were adopted by the trustees for use at the Institution. Coley was, therefore, familiar with Rule 43 that was drawn up 'To afford the trustees the power, if necessary, of dismissing either of the [two] annual surgeons'. As Rule 43 would be used against Coley in the months ahead following further publications of a circular and letters to the press, it is given in full and reads:

> Rule 43 – That, should either of the surgeons be found guilty of publishing any scandalous remarks respecting the professional character or conduct of his colleague or colleagues at the Infirmary, or be found guilty of any other immoral or dishonourable conduct, it shall be lawful for the trustees, at a Special General Meeting of them, to dismiss such surgeon so offending, if, upon a careful review of the case, and the report of the committee, they should find him guilty of the charges preferred against him.[41]

As we know, Coley was granted the position of Surgeon for Life and therefore Rule 43 could not, in theory, be applied to him. However, it could have been applied to Martin as an annual surgeon who, at the adjourned meeting of 12 March, was now willing to be reconciled with Coley. Another satisfactory result was that the notes appended to the minutes of 21 June 1838 should be 'erased' as they could 'cast the most serious imputations upon the character of Mr Williams [whose] imperfections [were] unfounded'. These 'expunged' and 'erased' notes of 14 and 21 June 1838 respectively, which are to be found in the Infirmary minute books at the Shrewsbury Archive centre, are deliberately obliterated. Pages are adhered together whilst further pages are made illegible.[42] Such a find was tantalising; however, after due consideration, it seemed appropriate that the adhered pages should remain sealed.

The reconciliation between Coley and Martin was short-lived as Martin, who had been given permission by the committee to extract the minutes of 4 March and forward them to the 'eight distant trustees' (in response to Coley's letter to the trustees) chose, according to Coley, to abuse his privilege by publishing an additional 30 copies, with a comment, for distribution throughout the town as well as exhibiting them at his lodgings.[43] Hence Coley's circular of 22 March in an effort to explain and defend his position that led the committee to call a further meeting on 5 April. At this meeting Coley was again accused of 'directly impeaching the truth'; of being 'liable to the Penalty of the 43rd Rule'; and that 'a Report of the same be laid before the Trustees'. Resolution 3 also stated:

> That the services of Mr Coley as Secretary to the committee be henceforth dispensed with, and that censure of his conduct be exposed for his having added in a most unwarrantable manner certain remarks of his own to the [illegible] of a requisition to call a meeting of the Committee for Friday April 5th, and on previous other occasions abusing the duties of his office.[44]

At this same meeting an unnamed person 'privately disclosed' to Coley that there were those who intended to provoke him into resigning his office of Surgeon for Life. Suitably alerted, Coley attended a meeting of the trustees, in the absence of the President, on 22 June 1839 where he is described as a 'dissentient'.[45] This disagreement with the official view resulted in the adjournment of the meeting, which reconvened on Saturday, 1 August with the President, Thomas Whitmore, in the chair. Others present included the Revd William Moore and John Lewis, a wine merchant and an early supporter of Coley, both of whom will be met with again when Coley publishes an open letter to the press. Meanwhile the nine trustees present (six of whom were also committee members), having considered the Infirmary Committees' report, passed a resolution which declared:

> That the Trustees upon a careful review of the case and of the report of the Committee find Mr Coley guilty of the charges preferred against him, and therefore in accordance with the 43rd Rule they forthwith dismiss him from the office of Surgeon at the Institution.[46]

A further resolution also stated that the house-apothecary, Mr Winchester, was to be called in and informed of Coley's dismissal. Although not stated in the minutes Winchester was now expected to work with Martin; a situation that he found untenable within weeks of Coley's dismissal due to Martin spreading 'scandalous rumours' about him. Needless to say the inevitable complaint by Winchester to the committee about Martin's behaviour fell on deaf ears. Was this a ploy by all concerned to isolate Coley from his competent and loyal house-apothecary? If it was, it partially succeeded as Winchester was peremptorily 'sacked' on 21 August for having absented himself from the Infirmary to attend his dying father without providing 'an approved substitute' during his absence; an accusation that was unfounded and one that was refuted by Coley.[47]

If the trustees and therefore the committee members thought that Coley would step aside gracefully to make way for Martin, they were mistaken. Determined to continue as before and now aware that their next intention was to deprive him of his trusteeship Coley continued, with great difficulty, to attend patients and undertake surgical procedures, assisted by Winchester, at the Infirmary where doors and cupboards were being locked against them and patients intimidated to prevent them from seeing Coley. To circumvent these problems Coley either forced open the doors, if the keys could not be found or, on occasion, resorted to taking a carpenter with him to make entry possible. Patients meanwhile voted with their feet and attended Coley at his house, whilst his in-patients, whose medicines were being withheld, were now supplied and paid for by Coley.[48]

Although Coley had been dismissed as Surgeon to the Infirmary on 1 August 1839, it is clear from the letter that follows that he continued to practice surgery. The letter also demonstrates the difficulties encountered not only by Coley but also by his in-patients: patients that he had instructed the Matron, Mrs Mary Griffiths, to care for; and specifically one William Kirkham of Madeley whose operation had taken place on 6 October. The open letter to the press,[49] which is long, is given in full as it not only offers Coley's perspective but also demonstrates, in part, both the vulnerability of a poor patient's position during this extraordinary period at the Infirmary and the power of some trustees and others, including Martin, to intervene in patient care. Patient Kirkham, who had undergone bilateral cataract surgery, would have had both his eyes bandaged and been required to keep his head immobilised for several weeks between sand bags. As a consequence, he would have required feeding and tending to by Matron Griffiths.

To the Rev. W. Moore.

Sir,

Having been informed that you and Mr Lewis went to the Bridgnorth Infirmary, on Tuesday, October 8th, to desire the Matron not to make up any more Beds, nor to supply food to my In patients, in consequence of hearing that I had successfully operated for Cataract in both eyes on William Kirkham, who had been blind five years, and had been discharged incurable from the Salop Infirmary;

I have considered it my duty, as Trustee and Surgeon for Life *to the Institution, to remind you that, when I founded the Charity, it was intended that through it the* "benefits of skill and humanity" *should be extended to every* "indigent person". *This poor man, for whom I have been so fortunate as to restore the blessings of sight, has a wife and ten children depending on him, and while he was blind and without any means of support, was of course* "indigent"; *and the benefits which he has experienced at my hands in conformity with the intentions of the Trustees, instead of exciting your disapprobation, ought to have filled your mind with satisfaction and delight. Had you a wife and ten children, looking up to you for support, and had you the misfortune to be blind, what would you think of a Minister of the Gospel, who was so devoid of* "Humanity", *as to endeavour to deprive you of the benefits of* "Skill", *by denying you a bed to lie upon and food for your support?*

With respect to Mr Lewis, he is not a Trustee to the Institution, and consequently not a Guardian of the rights of the Poor, and therefore I shall not take any notice of him; but you are highly censurable for attempting to *delegate to Mr MARTIN the privilege you do not possess of depriving the poor man of his bed and threatening to turn him out of the Institution, and annoying him by disturbing him at all hours in the night, and by the* most unfeeling conduct in the day.

Allow me to tell you that your profession of Christian faith will be of little avail, unless that faith be rendered manifest by good works.

You said that I might have recommended the patient to the Institution. *So I might, being the largest contributor in the town to its support; but as the Institution* could not operate, *of what more use would any recommendation have been, than that of the Subscriber, who recommended him to the Salop Infirmary?*

I intend this letter and the whole of the late proceedings to be published; and if you and the rest of the Committee wish to stand clear in the public estimation, the sooner you check Mr Martin's licentious conduct at the Infirmary the better.

   I am, Sir, your humble servant,
   J.M. Coley

What became of poor William Kirkham is unknown. What is known is that the committee admonished Matron Mary Griffiths for obeying Mr Coley's orders. As a consequence, she tendered her resignation ten days later.[50] One can only assume that her position became untenable due to conflicting orders over a duty of care to patient Kirkham that, unsurprisingly, led her to leave her post earlier than anticipated to be replaced by a Mrs Paget on 2 November.

Two weeks later, on 16 November, the trustees chose to place a demand upon Mrs J.M. Coley who, as the spinster Sarah Wainwright, had married the widower

James Milman in 1828. Since the inauguration of the Infirmary Mrs Coley, in conjunction with the wife of the Revd Knox Marshall, had been joint treasurers of the Benevolent Fund which provided in-patients with necessities, ordered by the surgeons, such as clothing and specifically foodstuffs to supplement certain patients' dietary needs, including port wine. The fund was also used to pay the wages of night nurses who were engaged to sit with the seriously ill or dying patient. Of the two women it was Mrs Coley who held the books and so, in accordance with the recently revised rules, she was required to provide a statement of account and transfer the balance of £10 10s 9d forthwith to the Revd Purton who, as treasurer to the Infirmary, now found himself treasurer of the Benevolent Fund with the subsequent task of preparing the accounts for the annual general meeting that would take place on 2 January 1840.

If the year of 1839 had been fraught with difficulties, the year of 1840 was to prove no better. Rumours must have proliferated in the town over Mrs Griffiths' sudden departure, as in January 1840 the Infirmary committee published a public notice.[51] This notice is in two parts: the first part, written by the committee, refutes certain allegations made by Coley over the reasons for Mrs Griffiths' departure which, according to the committee were: 'that her Salary was too small, and that her Health, which was not good, would probably be benefited by taking a situation in the Country'. To support their stance the committee contrived to involve Mrs Griffiths, whose letter below formed the second part of the notice.

Brierly Hill [*sic*], Jan. 13th. 1840

Gentlemen,

  I take the earliest opportunity of contradicting an assertion made and published by Mr. Coley, respecting the cause of my leaving the Infirmary. The part, which I allude to, is where he states that I left in consequence of the Committee being very angry and scolding me for giving the Patient Kirkham some food; now this I most positively deny; they told me I should not have done so, but they were not angry with me.

  The Account now published was read over to me previous to my Signature being to it, and I told Mr. Coley it was not correct; the Gentlemen were not angry with me, but said it shewed that I was tender hearted.

  The above statement was made in the presence of Mr. Mc.Michael.

          Your Obedient Servant,
            MARY GRIFFITHS

To the Committee of the
Bridgnorth Infirmary

From the above notice we learn that: 'The Account ... was read over to me previous to my signature ...' which suggests that Matron Griffiths was able to sign her name but unable to read writing, a situation that was not unusual at this time as illiteracy rates were high, particularly amongst women. However, this was also a time when patriarchy held sway and where class distinctions existed to the detriment of the 'lower orders' when subservience to one's 'betters' was the order of the day.

By 28 February (1840) it is clear that Coley had broken into the Infirmary again, as Mr Hallen, solicitor, is now instructed:

> to draw up and submit to the opinion of Counsel a case for his decision upon the point, where an action at Law would lie against Mr Coley for his late damage of the property belonging to the Institution, coupled with former acts of a similar character; and if not what mode of redress he would advise the Trustees to pursue.[52]

These 'former acts of a similar character' was a reference to: 'J.M. Coley ... breaking open the doors of the Infirmary and wilfully damaging the property of the said Trustees'[53] in the previous year. On that occasion the trustees wished Coley to be brought before them 'to answer sundry charges'. To that end the solicitor, Henry Vickers, was instructed to apply to the Borough Magistrates (all of whom were Whigs) for a summons to be placed upon Coley. As no record of a summons could be found it is assumed that the trustees failed in their endeavours to bring Coley before them. Nor, it would seem, were they successful in their attempts for 'an action at Law' against Coley, as nine weeks later Mr Hallen's bill is paid, which suggests advice rather than action was taken.

Come July, however, the tables were turned for it is minuted that Coley indicts the Medical Officers (Martin and the relatively new house-apothecary, Edward Toye Woodward) for assault. Placed on trial at Bridgnorth Quarter Sessions the jury found Martin and Woodward guilty, with a fine of one shilling and imprisonment until the fine was paid.[54] In response to this and Coley's continuing intrusion into the Infirmary a decision was made, possibly on the advice of Counsel, to hold a Special General Meeting at which the trustees, committee members and, for the first time, subscribers, would consider the state of the Infirmary and the 'desirability of executing a declaration of Trust'.

All met on the 5 November 1840 in the Board Room[55] which, in the previous year, had been redecorated with wallpaper at a cost of £3 12s. Of the nine Trustees present, including James Milman Coley, five were ministers of the Anglican Church. Also present were five committee members, two of whom were Anglican clergy, whilst the subscribers were represented by five local male worthies. Chaired by the President, Thomas Whitmore, the meeting acknowledged the difficulties between Mr Coley and Mr Martin that led to the 43rd Rule being invoked and the dismissal of Coley as surgeon. Concern was also expressed over the viability of the Infirmary with subscriptions down and many patients having deserted it. However, it was resolved that the Charity should continue, and therefore a formal Declaration of Trust was required. This legal document was to be drawn up by the solicitor, Mr Hallen, and laid before a second Special General Meeting on 3 December at which Coley was requested to attend. This opportunity would then permit Coley to examine the document and make any statements relevant to it. There is no record of a meeting on the 3 December 1840, nor is there any further mention of the late Senior Surgeon, Mr James Milman Coley.

One year later, on the 9 November 1841, the Aldermen and councillors of Bridgnorth elected one of their number, Mr James Milman Coley (now a committed Whig), as Mayor of Bridgnorth. This same year also saw Bridgnorth's Whig-led town council appointing a committee of enquiry into the Revd Dr Thomas Rowley's conduct at the Grammar School where, it was alleged, he was neglecting the foundation scholars.[56] Was this a political act against a 'staunch Tory' on the part of the Whigs or an attempt at restorative justice on behalf of Coley who had suffered humiliation at the hands of the clergy and particularly the Revd Rowley who had frequently chaired many of the Infirmary committee meetings? The question remains open, but in the following year Coley was, once again, elected Mayor of Bridgnorth. He would also serve on the Borough Magistrates Committee as its chairman,[57] thus indicating that no legal actions were brought against him.

From *Slater's Directory* of 1844 we find Coley still residing in Mill Street where he practiced as a 'Surgeon (Consulting)'. No longer Surgeon for Life and denied access to the Infirmary where his surgical skills could be utilised, Coley furthered his studies and on 23 December 1844 was admitted as a Licentiate of the Royal College of Physicians at the not inconsiderable age of 60. A year later he was listed as still living in Bridgnorth[58] but thereafter there is no reference to him other than the sale of his Mill Street property (valued at £1,912 12s 6d) which took place on the 9 October 1847 at the Crown Hotel, Bridgnorth.[59] It is therefore assumed that Coley arrived in London during 1846 to pursue his medical career having left behind an Infirmary that he was instrumental in founding and one that, in 1841, was re-established by those who sought to forget a troublesome past.

In a firm, clear copperplate hand there is an inscription on the opening page of a minute book[60] that declares:

Bridgnorth Infirmary
Established 1841

At the stroke of a pen, nine years were swept aside whilst further strokes were applied to an indenture between Thomas Whitmore, the lessee of the Infirmary building and its grounds, and others who, as Trustees of the Infirmary (that now excluded James Milman Coley), sought a new agreement. This indenture, dated March 25 1841, was conveyed 'for the sum of ten shillings of lawful British money ... for the purpose of founding and establishing an Infirmary for the relief of the sick poor of Bridgnorth'.[61] It is a date that has been perpetuated in directories and in more recent texts, including the Town Hall's chronological boards, which gives the year of the Infirmary's founding as 1842.

Ironically, the bickering did not cease with Coley's departure, as complaints and charges, brought on occasion by Martin, were made against the ever-changing house-apothecaries, whose title by 1842 became that of house-surgeon. Perversely (or so it seems) during 1843, and certainly by 1844, James Henry Martin had moved from his residence in High Town's Whitburn Street to Mill Street in Low Town – the preserve of Coley and his extended family – where he established a general medical practice. By 1851 Martin was married with two young children in a household that required the services of two servants and a groom. He had, by this time, also engaged a partner, Mr Richard Clarke Burleigh, LAC, MRCS (Lon) and an 18-year-old surgeon's apprentice by the name of Francis H. Homfray.

Established professionally, Martin now resigned from his various medical posts, including that of visiting surgeon to the Infirmary and that of a surgeon to the Bridgnorth Union (workhouse) where he also held the post of Superintendent Registrar.[62] His reasons for these resignations, including that of a town councillor (which suggests he had become an active and respected inhabitant of the town), are not known. His purpose, however, was to emigrate with his wife and children to New Zealand, which had become a British Colony in 1840. Arriving in February 1852 to a very different life as settlers in South Island, Mrs Martin would die in 1857, and James Henry Martin a decade later in July 1867.[63] Four months later another death occurred, that of the 83-year-old James Milman Coley, whose peripatetic life since leaving Bridgnorth had been spent in London, Brussels, Llandudno and finally London where he died on 11 November 1867 at St Peter's House in Kennington.[64]

Coley's death warranted a few lines in the *Bridgnorth Journal* but not an obituary for a man whose determination and organisational abilities were instrumental in founding the Bridgnorth Infirmary. However, the years of 1838–40 were contentious and fraught with stormy exchanges as personalities clashed in an institution that was fast becoming dysfunctional and whose viability was being questioned. The problem, according to the minute books (where bias should be a consideration) lay with Coley and his disregard for the 'Rules' in a world where 'Rules' were often viewed as inviolate. From Coley's *A Faithful Report* (pp. 28–9) we also glean an alternative perspective in which he felt 'compelled to defend [his] character, rights and privileges, which have been invaded for an express purpose ...' which was to deny him his rights as a trustee and deprive him of his position as Surgeon for Life at the Infirmary. Those that sought to oust him of his 'rights and privileges' were, without exception, all Tories. So too was Coley – initially – but from his various public statements there is also the suggestion that he was of a liberal disposition which, at some time during his exceptionally difficult period at the Infirmary, led him to align himself with the Whigs of Bridgnorth. As a political party the Whigs were open to new ideas and social reform, unlike the Tories whose desire was to retain the status quo; a philosophy that Coley must have questioned, as he would the actions of the Tory vicars during those distressing years of 1838 to 1840.

As a Whig, Coley would have been a lone voice at the Infirmary as many, including James Henry Martin, supported the Bridgnorth Conservative Association whose founding president was none other than Thomas Whitmore of Apley.[65] As a family the Whitmores were returned as Conservative members of Parliament generation after generation; so, at a time of social unrest, particularly when the Whigs came to Bridgnorth to contest the political dominance of the Whitmores and their fellow Conservatives, elections verged on the riotous during the 1830s and '40s. Many in the town, be they tenants, clergy or officials were often beholden to the Whitmores,[66] as were charities, including the Bridgnorth Infirmary that additionally sat upon Apley land. As a consequence many townspeople knew where their loyalties lay: with the Whitmores.

As for Coley, with his seemingly forceful personality that some may have construed as arrogance, there is a picture of a frustrated man who, through his letters to the press, exhibits a need to counteract the allegations made against him. An early Victorian 'whistle-blower' who contravened the rules in addition to other alleged acts by going public over activities at the Infirmary, he eventually must have realised that his influence and therefore his power was ebbing away after a struggle that had lasted for two years. Choosing to relinquish his association with the Infirmary, he also relinquished his original intentions, which were to 'provide relief to the poor', raise the 'usefulness of provincial surgery' and 'to promote medical science' in an infirmary where he had hoped to practice as a Surgeon for Life. This ambition denied doubtless left him an unfulfilled man whose leaving must also have affected many in the community including the 'deserving poor' who arguably benefited not only from his altruism but also from his skills as a surgical and medical practitioner in a small market town.

James Milman Coley's vision, however, would continue in a 'House' that met the needs of the day; as would those early 'untrained' nurses whose inadequacies, like those of the building, would gradually become apparent and therefore render them unfit for purpose at a time when changing values would, inevitably, necessitate change.

4   THE HOUSE

*That in a building so unsuitable for hospital work as the present Bridgnorth
Infirmary the inestimable gift of health has been restored to so many sufferers is due –
under God's blessing – to the great care and skill of doctors and nurses.*

*Mrs. Gamp, and her snuffy and bibulous colleagues, have passed away, "unwept,
unhonoured", if not "unsung", and have been replaced by highly trained and efficient
nurses, whose chief objects are not to save themselves trouble and to secure their
own ease, but to promote the comfort of the patients committed to their care, and to
alleviate their sufferings.*

Revd John P. Wright, Hon. Secretary, December 1893

E STABLISHMENTS that were known as an infirmary or a hospital each had a distinct purpose in mediaeval times. An infirmary or 'infirmarium', a sick bay, served the sick and wounded, whilst a hospital offered hospitality to the needy, aged and infirm. Both were served by religious communities (or houses) where descriptive terms such as 'bede-house' and 'lazer-house' came into being, as did the generic term, 'the House'.

It was this term, 'the House', that came to be used throughout the centuries, including the nineteenth century, when reference was made to either an infirmary or a hospital by those associated with its purpose. Today, it is used as an appellative to describe hospital doctors of a junior rank in teaching hospitals, for example: house physician, house-surgeon and, collectively, house officers.

With the development of the voluntary hospital movement during the eighteenth century the distinction between infirmary and hospital was perpetuated, but in a wider sense as hospital now included those 'Royal Hospitals' where the patronage of kings, and others, had added wealth and prestige to these long-established and rather grandiose institutions.[1] As a consequence hospitals became synonymous with wealthy 'royal' foundations, one being London's St Bartholomew's Hospital which was re-founded in 1546 and attended by James Milman Coley in 1806. According to Coley, patients were 'maintained by the funds of the institution'; it was therefore a system that invited abuse, particularly during the winter months, as there were those who would seek 'generous accommodation'. Perceived by Coley as a 'pernicious custom', it was one that would not prevail at Bridgnorth's Infirmary as he determined that patients would be charged for their weekly maintenance: 4s for the labouring poor and 6s for servants.[2]

By contrast an infirmary, as Stevenson remarks, 'always served the sick and wounded, though from a defined community' and as a term may have been used to distinguish its purpose: that of serving the working poor whilst simultaneously attempting to 'convey a becoming and rational modesty'.[3]

When Coley addressed the public meeting in 1832, he defined those who would use the Infirmary's services: the working poor who suffered either accidents or 'surgical diseases'. He also suggested that the number of residents in the town's two parishes of St Mary Magdalene and St Leonard, including 'a district of 7 miles in some directions, and 10 to 14 in others' had a population of 25,232,[4] all of whom could be served by the proposed 'small' infirmary. Thus Bridgnorth's medical charity, an infirmary, indicated to those in the community its intentions for a building which, unlike those large and well-endowed 'Royal Hospital' foundations, would indeed be small and modest by comparison.

As a building, 'the House' can still be viewed from Holly Bush Road where it looms comparatively large against an outcrop of sandstone on a south-facing hillside. Three storeys high, the unadorned façade with its central door and eight sash windows can be observed, as can the initial courses of irregular sandstone blocks that rise to meet Broseley brick and thence a slate roof, out of which emerge four chimney stacks, upon which numerous chimney pots remain.

Built on 'economic principles', it is assumed that the sandstone blocks that formed the initial courses were fashioned from the rock outcrop at the rear of the building, as a 'cavity in the rock' was formed which housed the boilers for heating the baths. This same cavity or cave (a feature of some older Bridgnorth properties) would, in 1885, become a mortuary. In that same year, it was also minuted[5] that two rooms abutted 'a portion of the rock' thus causing them 'to be very damp and almost unusable', a problem that was temporarily addressed by excavation.

However, damp rooms were not the only problem as the location of the House, and therefore access to it, also created difficulties, as a reported speech by the Bishop of Hereford identified in 1890:

When they thought of the locality in which the present building stood, when they thought of the necessity of all patients being brought down those terrible steps – he [the Bishop] looked at them with considerable anxiety, and thought the danger might be apprehended from them – there surely was sufficient reason for asking for a new building.[6]

The 'terrible steps' in question were a series of steep steps, off Listley Street, that required negotiating to gain access to the rear entrance of the building. Built in 1836, the steps were also used by the various Matrons to obtain water from the conduit that was situated on Listley Street. This was until, at some date, water tanks were installed: one in the roof with a capacity of approximately 500 gallons and another 'outside' that stored about 200 gallons of 'soft water',[7] possibly situated adjacent to a detached wash house erected in 1885.

The main entrance at the front of the building was, however, the accepted entrance for those patients 'who had received serious accidents'. Approached from Holly Bush Road, patients were transported up a 'long flight of steps' in a 'carrying chair' that, by 1885, was recognised as being 'not suitable for all cases' and indeed 'was often a cause of great suffering to those who had received serious accidents'. To alleviate such suffering, the external works of 1885 included the removal of the steps below the building, which were replaced by a 'winding path' so that patients could be 'conveyed to the Infirmary without being jolted at every step'.

Once inside the house, each of the 13 rooms[8] was utilised for a specific purpose. From the minutes of 1885, when the parlous state of the Infirmary required 'modernisation', some indication of its internal arrangements can be deduced, as they also can from a valuation report[9] of 1896 when preparations for the sale of the Infirmary were taking place (see Table 2).

From the table it is apparent that room usage changed with the 'modernisation' of the Infirmary, as it had in previous years, when sanitary arrangements were introduced. However, Table 2 does not identify certain rooms or where they were located within the building. For example, a Board Room is not listed where once the Trustees and committee members would meet to conduct the business of the institution. Comfortably appointed, the walls were papered, the floor carpeted and suitable furniture and furnishings installed.

There was also a room that, in 1836, was described as a 'surgery' and for which two articles were purchased: an oil cloth, four yards by three yards (thus indicating that the material may have been used to cover a table upon which surgical procedures took place) and a set of fire irons, which suggests that an open fire existed in the room.[10] Where this room was located is not known; however, from the valuation report an 'operating room' was situated on the first floor and described as such in May 1865 when an estimate was

Table 2. Bridgnorth Infirmary: internal arrangement of rooms in 1885[A] and at valuation in 1896[B]

Existing Rooms	Alterations and Improvements	Change of use in 1885 to:	At valuation in 1896
GROUND FLOOR		Detached wash-house built, stove, piping	+ Galvanized soft water tank, 200 gallon
Old Front Kitchen	Boarded floor laid, new fireplace, furnishings	Matron Hadfield's sitting room	Sitting room, gas pendant, roller blind
Old Brew house	A new range, cupboard, drying rods	Kitchen	Kitchen and scullery with speaking tube
Larder	Whitewashed and ventilation improved	Larder	Pantry
Entrance Hall	Linen press put up	Entrance hall	Entrance Hall. Gas bracket and shade
FIRST FLOOR			**First Floor Entrance Hall**
Old 'useless' Bathroom		Out-patient waiting room	Waiting room
Small room	Next to old bathroom	Dispensary	Dispensary: 5 x 6' shelves, oak table
Old Dispensary	Furnishings	House-surgeon's bedroom	Surgeon's room, outside sun blind
Sitting room for house-surgeon	New furniture	House-surgeon's sitting room	Private room
Ward No. 1 *Operating room recorded in valuation on first floor*	Painted, furnished with 3 iron bedsteads, 3 wire-spring mattresses, bedding, 3 lockers, 3 medicine brackets and a table	Ward No. 1: 3 beds	Large room (front) Ward. Another Large Room (back) is also recorded
UPPER FLOOR		Water Closet (W.C.)	W.C. and passage
Old Matron's Bedroom	Furnished as Ward No. 1	Additional Ward – now No. 2: 3 beds	Large room (front) Ward
Ward No. 2	Furnished in similar way	Now Ward No. 3: 3 beds	Another large front room
Small Ward	Repainted	Now No. 4: Isolation/ serious cases: 2 beds	Smaller front room
Old house-surgeon's bedroom	Repainted	Matron's bedroom	Back room – (? Matron's bedroom)
Servants' Bedroom	Repainted	Servants' bedroom	Back room – (? Servants' bedroom)
Closet No. 1 (lumber store)	New bath, heated by gas	Bathroom	Bathroom, basin. Boiler tank in roof
Closet No. 2 (lumber store)	Sink and shelves fitted	Matron's scullery for washing dressings	Wash-up closet: 4 shelves, iron lintel and fittings
WALLS & CORRIDORS	Repainted a 'cheerful colour with a high varnished dado of a dark colour'		
UPPER CORRIDOR	Bells, 2 knockers, 11 fingerplates, table		

Sources: A SA 2740/10 Bridgnorth Infirmary, Report and Balance Sheet for 1885
    B SA 4752/59/101 Nock, Deighton & Kirby, Valuation Book 1896–1897. Folio No. 1

accepted for installing gas lighting. What is certain is that in January 1890 the operating room was deemed 'quite unfit for the purposes for which it was used'.[11]

One room that appears to have remained constant in its location on the first floor was the dispensary, which was described in 1885 as 'one of the largest and best rooms in the house'. Seemingly unused during the Infirmary's early years, in January 1839 the subscribers to the Bridgnorth Dispensary, having apparently vacated their rented room with the introduction of a domiciliary service, offered their fixtures to the Infirmary's Trustees, which were duly accepted. Placed into storage, the fixtures were eventually installed in 1842 when a carpenter was employed for 'fitting up [the] dispensary' at a time when the Infirmary's finances, always precarious, had improved due to a 'Legacy' and a 'liberal donation' that enabled the paying off of monies borrowed on the building.[12]

A ground floor room, allocated as a brew house, was also 'modernised' in 1885 with the introduction of a new range, a large cupboard and 'all things necessary for a kitchen'. That a brew house existed, where the brewing of beer would have been undertaken by the Matron, was not unusual, as the consumption of alcoholic drinks by patients and staff alike was a common activity – as it was amongst the population at large (the latter being demonstrated, in part, by the Bridgnorth diarist George Gitton[13] who was a jobbing printer and newspaper reporter for Mr Watton, the owner of the *Shrewsbury Chronicle*). There was also 'a common belief that water required purification with spirits and that, generally, intoxicants were important aids to physical stamina, virility and health'.[14] As Bridgnorth's untreated Severn water supply was situated 'below where many of the sewers emptied themselves into the river'[15] it is suggested that brewing was partly a recognition of the unwholesome state of the water, as beer was presumably considered safer and more pleasant to drink than Severn water. There was also a supply of spring water; however it did not extend to all parts of the town until the late 1890s.

There is also some uncertainty about the location of the water closets (W.C.s) that appear to have been situated on the upper floor as Closets 1 and 2. However, these were described in 1885 as containing lumber and the sanitary arrangement as 'bad and defective': a problem that was remedied by 'a properly constructed W.C.' on the upper floor during 1885. When the Infirmary opened in 1836 the purchase of chamber ware (earthenware chamber pots) was recorded – six pots for the three wards and one set, with bowl and ewer, for the surgeon's room – which suggests that sanitary arrangements were primitive. Similarly, there is no reference to an outdoor privy being built at this or any other time. However, in 1849 a second outbreak of cholera occurred in the town, during which 75 persons died of the disease. This prompted an Inquiry under the Public Health Act[16] of 1848 into the sanitary state of Bridgnorth where the average mortality rate, between the years of 1845 to 1849, was 32 persons in every 1,000. Published in 1853, the Report's findings spoke of 'numerous cesspools' and 'liquid refuse from defective drains' within the town, which the author clearly associated with the unacceptable high mortality and sickness rates amongst the population.[17]

A direct result of the Report was a commitment on the part of the Infirmary's administrators and the Local Board of Health to construct two water closets, including a drainage system, that were installed during 1856 at a cost of £32 1s. However, it is unlikely that the drainage system would have been connected to a sewer at that time as the High Town Drainage Plan, although said to be progressing well in 1856, was slow and difficult to implement.[18] A further 'modernisation' was the structural alteration to the window in the staircase, which was raised 'to improve the ventilation to the second floor and give more light' whilst a dust-hole was 'done away with' and covered over for the storage of two galvanized iron buckets as dust receptacles.

Irrespective of the Infirmary's physical disadvantages, patients and staff alike were prepared to enter its doors and accept the constraints that the building and its location imposed upon all who entered. Those charged with administering the daily routines of the Infirmary were the House-Surgeon and the Matron, and it is here that we turn to the Reverend Wright's comments[19] on nurses, and specifically his reference to Mrs Gamp, a nurse whom Charles Dickens characterised in his novel *Martin Chuzzlewit*, published in 1843/4. Dickens considered that his portrayal of the widow, Mrs Sarah Gamp, was a fair representation of a nurse in the early nineteenth century. Described as being a 'fat old woman with a husky voice and a moist eye' who dressed in a 'very rusty black gown, rather the worse for snuff', Mrs Gamp also had a propensity to imbibe spirits.[20] In describing this fictional character whose fictional colleague, Mrs Betsy Prigg, 'was recommended from Bartholomew's' (St Bartholomew's Hospital, London), Dickens partially reveals the tasks undertaken by early nineteenth-century nurses who, as independent practitioners, were often illiterate and working class. Employed by the rich and poor alike to care for the sick, infirm or pregnant in their own homes, these domiciliary nurses were variously described as a sick-nurse, a monthly-nurse and a day-nurse whose work included 'night-watching' and 'a laying-out' of the dead. They also attended 'a lying-in' of women in childbirth, thereby combining midwifery with nursing (as demonstrated by the erstwhile Mrs Gamp), whilst Mrs Prigg – and her non-fictional practitioners – was also additionally employed in hospitals.[21]

As an occupation, nursing was unstructured and unregulated, whilst the practitioners, whose knowledge and skills were largely based upon experiential learning, were deemed uneducated and unrefined, which, as Summers suggests:

> … *offended a growing and many-stranded movement for nursing reform for reasons which had little to do with their clinical proficiency. Male physicians and surgeons, religious reformers of both sexes, and all those anxious to expand professional opportunities for women, combined both consciously and unconsciously to deny Mrs Gamp and her ilk a respected place in the provision of care for the sick.*[22]

These women, so engagingly portrayed by Dickens, provide an image that became synonymous with the 'untrained' nurse during the latter part of the nineteenth century, and one that has since endured, thereby denying the sober, biddable, kindly and often illiterate 'untrained' nurse her place in nursing history. Perhaps a more representative description of the 'untrained' nurse may be gained from Sir James Paget (1814–1899) of St Bartholomew's Hospital who, in 1830, recalled that the nurses were: 'dull, unobservant, and untaught women; of the best it could only be said that they were kindly and careful, and attentive in doing what they were told to do'.[23]

From those records that exist, where little information on the Matrons of the Bridgnorth Infirmary is to be had [see Table 3], it is clear that none of the early 'untrained' Matrons were instantly dismissed for being either 'snuffy' or 'bibulous'. Indeed there is an impression that the conscientious laboured long hours with varying degrees of ability over domestic chores that included washing the house-surgeon's linen, making up beds, purchasing foodstuffs and preparing food for patients, even when some matrons were elderly or infirm. Once employed, there were some matrons who continued to work 'past their art' as the concept of retirement in conjunction with a State Pension would not be realised until the twentieth century. Benefits therefore were few; however, the post did bring with it a roof over the head for both the matron and her family, a bed in which to sleep and food to sustain a working day; conveniences that were not always available to the patients they served, many of whom lived in substandard dwellings and whose poverty resulted in a lack of food and clothing. These factors would later be exposed in a report on Bridgnorth's sanitary state, and were subsequently reflected at the Infirmary where sanitary arrangements were inadequate and the diet of patients meagre in a 'House' that gradually became unfit for purpose, as did the 'untrained' matrons who tended the sick.

'Elected' to the post by the Infirmary committee, Matrons were paid quarterly, often in arrears, by the treasurer. Notice to terminate employment, by either side, was also quarterly. However, once a notice was served, a replacement was immediately sought and upon 'election' the Matron appears to have entered her post within a matter of weeks rather than months, thus indicating that the three-month notice to terminate was not strictly adhered to by either side. As a consequence, those columns relating to the commencement and termination of employment in Table 3 are tentative, as some dates could not be positively confirmed, except where exact dates are given.

All the Matrons, including those with family members, were resident at the Infirmary where accommodation was restricted – probably to one room – and for which there appears to have been no charge for board and lodging. Some husbands, however, did undertake paid work at the Infirmary, which included general repairs and portering duties. The Matrons would also have taken their orders from, and been answerable to, the honorary surgeons, and by extension the Infirmary Committee,

Table 3. Matrons of the Bridgnorth Infirmary 1836–1921. NB: *both ages and employment dates are tentative, except where exact dates are given.*

Name	Title	Age at appointment	Commenced employment	Terminated employment	Salary commencing	Remarks
Collins	Mrs	unknown	25 July 1836	? Oct. 1837	£20 annually	Agreed to officiate as Matron
Griffiths, Mary (? widow)	Mrs	unknown	13 Oct. 1837	? Oct. 1839	£26 annually	Son permitted as lodger. Tenders resignation 16/10/1839
Paget, Elizabeth	Mrs	56 years	2 Nov. 1839	? July 1841	£30 annually	Tenders resignation 3/6/1841
Powell	Mrs	unknown	26 July 1841	? April 1847	£30 annually	'Fit and proper person.' Tenders resignation 4/2/1847
Cheese, Mary	Mrs	57 years	28 April 1847	26 April 1851	£35 annually	'Increasing infirmities'. To resign
Robinson, Elizabeth	Mrs	55 years	? April 1851	1 July 1869	£35 annually	'Unable to perform duties'. Not required after 1/7/1869. Presented £10 for long service
Cheese, Martha	Miss	44 years	1 July 1869	? 1874	£40 annually	Minute of 2/12/1870: 'to receive notice'. Daughter of Matron Mary Cheese
Matron: ? Martha Cheese and also 'The Nurse' in 1871.					'Matron' £10 in 1870 £50 p.a. 1871	Training of Matron at 'St. John's Hospital, London' for 6 months at a cost of £12. Martha resident at 7/8 Norfolk St, Strand, London, leased to St. John's Hospital, April 2, 1871
Sutherland, Mary (widow) Acting Matron	Mrs	57 years	unknown	unknown	£22.15s.0d	'Wages' in Matron's absence. 1871 Census = 'Matron of House'
Jones	Mrs	unknown	? 1874	? 1876	£60 in 1875	Name recorded in Treasurer's book
Thomas, Harriet	Mrs	50 years	? 1876	? June 1885	£30 annually	'Unable to perform duties'. To resign. Presented £20 for long service
Hadfield, Frances but known as 'Fanny'	Miss	31 years confirmed	24 June 1885	Departed Jan. 1895	£60 annually	'A trained Nurse of a higher class'. Salary in 1890 at £75 + £70 allowance for servants
Bailie, Hannah Mary, also referred to as 'Nina'	Miss	34 years	App'd 20/12/94 In post Jan. 1895	Departed Jan. 1921	£50 for 1896 £100 for 1920	Trained Nurse. Awarded RRC 1st Class, 1919. 26 years' service

Sources: Derived from SA 2740 /1 to 10; Bridgnorth Hospital Records; AGM reports and Census Returns

which was responsible for engaging and terminating their services. The early 'Rules' of the Infirmary, which would have incorporated 'Rules for Matrons', are no longer extant, but some indication of their responsibilities can be had from those matrons who worked at the Salop Infirmary, where patients were instructed to regard the matron as the 'Mistress of the House'.

As early matrons and nurses tended to be drawn from the domestic classes we find that the matrons of the Salop Infirmary were responsible for the general management and care of all the household goods and furniture. They were also responsible for the preparation of the 'diet', which included the supervising of patient meals at the right time and ensuring that they ate every scrap; the brewing of beer for which, if found wanting, the matron was reprimanded; and the total responsibility for provisions, including prevention of theft and the purchasing of foodstuffs that were not covered by any contract. Other duties included a twice-daily roll-call of patients and the recording of those who were absent in the Visitor's Book, whilst another twice-daily routine was the inspection of beds, clothing and linen to ascertain the state of their cleanliness. It was also the matron's responsibility to ensure that each patient had clean sheets upon admission, which remained in use for 14 days unless a directive from a physician ordered otherwise. A holder of keys, a supplier of medicines to patients and a reporter to the Weekly Board of improper behaviour of nurses, servants and patients alike, the matron was also 'ordered to attend Prayers every day and see that such patients did likewise'.[24]

Conceivably, the duties of the matrons at the Bridgnorth Infirmary were not dissimilar, but on a reduced scale, as the Salop Infirmary was a comparatively large institution that would not be assigned the prefix 'Royal' until 4 July 1914, when this was bestowed by King George V. However, other aspects of Bridgnorth's small infirmary varied considerably from the county establishment, as neither nurses nor servants were employed to assist the matron in her daily chores. On occasion, a woman was employed to undertake washing, which was a labour-intensive activity involving the hand-washing of sheets and other linens with boiling water and various chemical agents that produced a steamy and unpleasant environment. Nor did the Bridgnorth Infirmary possess a chapel; however, in-patients were supplied with bibles and prayer books that presumably few patients, if any, could read. There was also a Visitor's Book in which visitors (initially male committee members and later 'ladies') were requested to place remarks, and where comments or complaints from patients, staff and visitors could be recorded and inspected by the Infirmary Committee in pursuance of their administrative responsibilities. As the committee met quarterly, rather than weekly, the daily management of the House was left to the matrons who, in many respects, were untrained for such responsibilities; a situation that would not be addressed until 1883 when the competencies of the Infirmary's 'untrained' matron would come into question.

With the opening of the Infirmary in February 1836 the committee engaged a Mrs Cooksey. Employed on a temporary basis at 2s 6d per week for 'cleaning and taking care of the Infirmary', her duties included waiting upon the house-apothecary and the washing of his bed and table linen. Upon the cessation of Mrs Cooksey's employment, a Mrs Collins 'agreed to officiate as Matron to the Institution' on 21 June 1836. Employed from 25 July, initially for a period of six months, she commenced her duties on an annual salary of £20. Her tenure, which was extended, went unremarked, as did her departure, for on 13 October 1837 Mrs Mary Griffiths (previously mentioned in Chapter 3) was appointed and, as Matron, was to 'receive a salary of ten shillings per week and be allowed to have her son as a lodger'. Whether Mrs Griffiths was a widow or a deserted wife is unknown, but the fact that her son was allowed to reside with her suggests that he was young, as she too might have been.

Her work must also have been acceptable to the committee, for in January 1838 her salary was increased to £30 per annum. That same year also saw Mrs Griffiths receiving additional payments of 6s 6d for 'carrying water during the frost' and 7s 6d for 'sitting up for five nights' with presumably a very sick or dying patient; duties that were doubtless in addition to her daily chores that now included the purchasing of mops, brushes, buckets, black lead, sand and bath bricks 'for use of the Institution'. In a contractual arrangement, Matron was awarded an annual sum of one guinea (£1 1s) for domestic necessities that reflect a life of cleaning and scrubbing. Black lead would have been used to burnish the fireplace surrounds and brew house range; the grates having first been cleared, the range flue brushed and the fires made up. Meanwhile, the purchase of sand suggests that it may have been used for the absorption of spilt bodily fluids, including blood-loss during surgery. Alternatively, sand may also have been used for polishing domestic utensils, such as pots and pans.

There is, however, some uncertainty over the use of bath bricks, which may have been heated to maintain the heat of the bath water or to warm cold bath water. From its inception, the Infirmary provided 'shower baths' or 'plain water baths', either cold or warm, that members of the public were entitled to use upon payment of 6d for the former or 1s for the latter. The monies raised from this facility provided a very modest income that, at the height of its usage in 1853 (the year of the Sanitary Report) raised £2 1s 6d.[25] Baths, whether cold or warm but definitely not hot, were considered by some to have health-promoting properties during the nineteenth century; thus a cold bath was advocated for strengthening the internal organs, whilst a warm bath was considered advantageous for the general nervous system.[26]

We learnt earlier of the difficulties of the 'tender hearted' Matron Griffiths (a seemingly conscientious woman) concerning the patient Kirkham in the Autumn of 1839. This led her to give notice on 16 October 1839, only to be speedily replaced on 2 November by a Mrs Elizabeth Paget, aged 56 (married to William, a gardener some 14 years her senior). Having appointed Mrs Paget, perhaps in haste, on an annual salary of £30, by April 1840 the committee instructed Mrs Paget that the in-patients were no longer to pay her their 4s each for weekly maintenance. Instead, payments were to go directly to the treasurer, which suggests that the Committee kept a close watch on the accounts and that Matron Paget was perceived as being incompetent in financial matters. Alternatively, and arguably a more likely scenario is that the Committee, in their endeavours to thwart Coley (who, at this time, was paying the Matron a weekly food allowance for his patients) was desirous, if not intent, on curtailing his activities. Whatever the reasons, Mrs Paget tendered her resignation on 3 June, 1841, giving three months' notice to the committee who now sought a 'fit and proper person'.

On 18 June 1841 an advertisement appeared in the *Ten Towns Messenger* that read:

BRIDGNORTH INFIRMARY

WANTED a MATRON to the above Institution.
Testimonials of character for honesty, sobriety,
cleanliness, and kindness of disposition, will
be required.

  Applications to be addressed to the Secretary,
  Mr John Lewis, High Street.
  June 16, 1941 [a typographic error that should have read 1841][27]

Duly elected on 13 July 1841 to the post of Matron as a 'fit and proper person' was one Mrs Powell. Little is known of Mrs Powell or her circumstances other than that she commenced her duties on 26 July on an annual salary of £30, which appears to have remained constant throughout her employment. However, she was paid additional monies for undertaking 'washing'. Giving 'a quarters notice' on 4 February 1847 she was replaced by Mrs Mary Cheese. Appointed on 8 April, Mrs Cheese commenced her duties as Matron on 28 April 1847 at the age of 57 years, on an annual salary of £35.

Matron Cheese was accompanied by family members, including her husband Edward. Some seven years her junior and a bricklayer, he was known to have installed a new grate and frame for the furnace during his wife's tenure. Their unmarried 22-year-old daughter, Martha, who was described as a 'nurse', also lived at the Infirmary and may have assisted her mother in her duties. However, there is no record of payment to her until 1869 when Martha became the Matron. There was also a seven-year-old niece of whom no mention is made, except that she appeared on the 1851 census as being resident at the Infirmary.

Upon Matron Cheese's appointment in April, the committee recorded: 'That for the next three months the sum of 5s each weekly be allowed to the Matron for the maintenance of the In-Patients, in consideration of the high prices of Provisions'. It was an allowance that was reduced to 4s 6d in November and one that was to apparently cease on 25 December 1847. The 'high prices of Provisions' related to an insufficient supply of foodstuffs that was associated nationally with a rapidly expanding population, industrialisation, logistical problems in transportation and an embryonic retail system; as a consequence, the period subsequently became known as the 'Hungry Forties'.[28]

Meanwhile, during the following year of 1848, a 'charge' was brought against the house-surgeon and Matron Cheese when both were accused of neglecting an in-patient by the name of Thomas Wotton, who later died. The allegation, which was investigated by the committee, was found to be 'groundless'. How formal or thorough this investigation was went unrecorded, but every complaint was reviewed and commented upon, albeit briefly, in the minute books: (the exception being the Coley affair). Certainly complaints and complaint procedures were a facet of the voluntary hospital movement since its inception in the eighteenth century, for any slur could conceivably discourage benefactors and subscribers from providing largess; a state of affairs that had to be avoided as all medical charities depended on them financially for their very existence.[29]

With the reappearance of cholera in 1849 a degree of anxiety must have existed amongst the population at large, as the Infirmary's out-patient figures for the year totalled 1,069 (an increase of 165 persons on the previous year). Whether or not these figures included domiciliary visits is unrecorded, but as contagious diseases and 'fevers' of all descriptions were exempt from the Infirmary (as were other conditions), those who suffered would have languished in their caves or cave-houses – particularly in the streets of Cartway, Friars-Lane [sic] and Severns-side [sic] where dwellings were small, badly constructed and crowded together. Some of the sick would have waited upon the attendance of the Infirmary's house-surgeon, Mr Sydney Stedman Smith, whose domiciliary visits to the working poor were acknowledged by the committee when noting his 'efficient services … especially during the prevalence of the late alarming visitation of cholera'. From the undated medical evidence submitted to the inquiry into the sanitary state of Bridgnorth, some indication of the wretched state of the working poor is partially revealed. From a report of Stedman Smith's statement to the inquiry we learn:

> That his practice was confined exclusively to the infirmary, where about three fourths of the cases were those of persons living in the town. His patients were, for the most part, of the poorest class; and in many cases he considered that illness was brought on amongst them by want of food and clothing. During last year there had been fever [typhus] and scarlatina [scarlet fever], and low fever [typhoid] was then prevalent; in the course of his visits he met with many nuisances [objectionable substances] of various kinds that had a tendency to produce disease.

The medical officer for St Leonard's parish, William Thursfield (senior), also considered that 'too many of the lower classes [were] badly clothed and fed' and that in many cases they were also 'extremely dirty in their habits'. Alfred Mathias, medical officer for St Mary's parish, reported that 'he had only five cases of typhus fever' – the famine fever – and that privies in Underhill Street had 'house drains' running along the surfaces of kitchen floors.[30]

Inadequate food supplies combined with poor social conditions were therefore deemed by Bridgnorth's medical men to have a detrimental effect upon the health of the working poor, which Oddy places in context:

> For many people, diets limited by income and availability of food materials meant low nutritional status, poor health and restricted physical growth. It is difficult to disentangle the relationships between nutritional status, physical environment and the incidence of infectious diseases, but tuberculosis and gastro-intestinal fevers were endemic for most of the nineteenth century and nutritional deficiency diseases such as rickets and scurvy were also present.[31]

Four years after her appointment, Matron Cheese entered upon her 61st year 'in increasing infirmities'. It was therefore mutually agreed 'that she should resign her situation on 26 April, 1851'. Her replacement was Mrs Elizabeth Robinson who appeared cautious about giving her age as variations were noted in the decennial censuses (a phenomenon that is recognised, as are other discrepancies, in census returns).[32] Aged about 55 years upon entering her employment, Mrs Robinson was appointed on a salary of £35 per annum, which appears to have remained unchanged for 18 years. She was also married to John, a shoemaker, who undertook portering work at the Infirmary, including the delivery of notices of meetings for which he was paid 6s annually. Their eldest daughter was also resident at the Infirmary and described as a 'house servant', but whether of the Infirmary or a private dwelling is unknown.

During 1853 the high prices of provisions reappeared and again the Matron was allowed 4s 6d instead of 4s for each patient. It was a situation that appears to have continued into the following year of 1854 when, on April 6, the committee decided that the medical staff should draw up a new diet for the in-patients. On 4 May, each patient was now to receive the altered diet for the next three months, which was to cost 6s a head and consist of:

    1oz of butter per diem [daily]
    one pint of beer for dinner [i.e. lunch]
    one pint of good tea at 5 o'clock and
    one pint of milk, broth, or rice gruel at 8½ o'clock[33]

A contributing factor towards the high price of foodstuffs appears to be associated with the increasing numbers of patients undergoing surgical procedures that were variously described as either 'tedious' or 'protracted' (and, in particular, the lengthy stay of two in-patients, which lasted 'for many months'). Perhaps another factor was the declaration of war on 28 March 1854 by Britain and France on Russia, as any war has a tendency to disrupt food supplies and therefore increase costs. The hostility in question was the Crimean War (1854–56) that saw the redoubtable Miss Florence Nightingale (1820–1910), a lady of some standing in English society, arrive at Scutari on 4 November 1854 with a team of 38 nurses to tend the sick and wounded British soldiers.

In reality, Miss Nightingale became an administrator who gave a chaotic British military hospital and its environment some semblance of order, where the care of the diseased and wounded became a priority. Her indefatigable zeal and organisational abilities would, within a few years, turn towards the reform of nursing when a Training School for Nurses would be established at London's St Thomas' Hospital (a 'Royal' foundation) in 1860. The purpose of the training school was to turn nursing from a despised occupation into a 'respectable profession'. To that end, only 'ladies' with a high moral character were accepted as probationers (student nurses) and having gained a certificate were then expected to accept posts in hospitals elsewhere.[34] In time, other training schools for nurses were established which, in their turn, would also produce the 'highly trained and efficient nurses' so esteemed by the Revd J. Wright in 1893. It was a scheme that would ultimately replace the 'untrained' nurse – but not in Bridgnorth for some years to come.

Meanwhile, the year of 1863 witnessed a severe epidemic of scarlet fever that had so 'fatally prevailed' in the town and neighbourhood, particularly 'among the poor'. Out-patient figures reached 1,312, of whom 13 were recorded as dying. Again the 'well-known skilful House Surgeon', Mr Sydney Stedman Smith, visited the poor and was duly rewarded for his services to them with a gratuity of £10 upon his resignation in 1865, after 17 years of toil at the Infirmary.

During the following year, a Mr Cameron was appointed as house-surgeon to the Infirmary where he received, on 13 November 1866, a railway employee suffering from a severe injury. The event was recorded in George Gitton's diary[35] in which he wrote:

Tuesday 13 November: … *Accident at 8 on railway. James Hamblin, guard, fractured his leg & taken to Infirmary* …

Wednesday 14 November: … *After dinner went down to Infirmary & saw Cameron, house surgeon, & the sufferer, guard Hamblin. He was sleeping in a stupor!* [A stupor that may have been induced by the administration of either alcohol or opium or both to alleviate pain]. *After at railway station. Met Haines*

& the new station master, Isaac Norris Hunt. Heard particulars of yesterday's accident … after tea sent off full account of that and railway accident to Watton's Salop paper by 7.35 post. Put in by Susan [Gitton's housekeeper and companion] who afterwards fetched in pills & rum from Deighton's, 7d. Shaved by Botwood at 8.30 this evening.

Gitton's report to Watton's paper, the *Shrewsbury Chronicle*,[36] was published two days later:

BRIDGNORTH RAILWAY ACCIDENT

On Tuesday night last about 8 o'clock, an alarming occurrence took place at our railway station. One of the guards of the Shrewsbury train, named John Hamblin, was engaged amongst the carriages, when he slipped and got his leg between the wheel of one of them and the rails. The poor fellow's leg was broken, and it was thought that it would have to be taken off. He was conveyed immediately to the Infirmary, and received every assistance from the house surgeon, Mr Cameron.

Mr Cameron's 'every assistance' proved futile as Gitton recorded:

Wednesday 5 December: … *Inquest on James Hamblin, railway guard, at Infirmary, died from accident November 13* …

In George Gitton's unpublished diaries for 1883 and 1884, Gitton not only describes his own illnesses and treatments but also the last illness of Susan, his housekeeper and companion, who attended the Infirmary as an out-patient where she received 'her medicines.' Said by Gitton to be 'Very bad with Cold and Bronchitis' on Wednesday 14 November 1883, Susan died almost a year to the day later, on Monday 10 November 1884, at the age of 70, when Gitton recorded:

> … *Susan still kept on in dreadful Trial & Agony which went all morning and continued till evening at 5 or 6. After Dreadful Pangs & pain – At 12 o'c Mrs Goodall came up to her & about 1 o'clock poor Susan breathed her last and died serenely quiet: Mrs Goodall, Mrs Lowe and Lydia Foxall all up with her & at 3 o' clock in Morning they laid her out* …[37]

The last offices, or laying-out of the dead, was a solemn task undertaken by women; a duty that Matron Robinson would doubtless have performed upon the death of James Hamblin in 1866. By March 1869, Matron Robinson was either nearing or in her early

70s, and 'being no longer equal to her duties, she shall receive three months notice and that another Matron be engaged to succeed her'. With her services no longer required after 1 July, she was presented with a sum of £10 in recognition of her long service.

In her place came Miss Martha Cheese who was duly elected as Matron on 3 June on a salary of £40 per annum. Aged 44 and the daughter of Mary Cheese, a previous Matron, Martha entered her duties on 1 July 1869, only to be given notice in December 1870 due to pending organisational changes at the Infirmary.

From the Infirmary's inception there had been a desire on the part of its founders to amalgamate the town's existing Dispensary with the Infirmary. Approaches had been made to the Dispensary committee in the early 1830s and again during December 1842, but all proposals to unite Bridgnorth's two medical charities were firmly rebuffed by the members of the Dispensary committee.

Twenty-eight years later, when many of the old guard had either died or moved on, a new optimism prevailed. At a joint meeting of the Infirmary and Dispensary committees, held on 29 November 1870 and chaired by Mr Thomas Martin Southwell, Mayor of Bridgnorth (who was shortly to be elected as a Trustee of the Infirmary) the subscribers and committee members of both institutions came together to hear a proposition put before them by William Orme Foster Esq., the new owner of Apley Park, who proposed:

> that from after the 1st day of January 1871 this Institution be amalgamated with the Bridgnorth Dispensary and that the joint Institution be called the Bridgnorth Infirmary and Dispensary.

Seconded by the Revd George Leigh Wasey of Quatford, the proposal was carried unanimously, as was a second proposal that a committee of 'Gentlemen' be formed to:

> arrange all the details immediately to enable the Joint Institution to commence operations on the 1st day of January 1871 or as soon afterwards as can be conveniently be done.[38]

On 3 January 1871 the Infirmary's Committee of Management[39] called another meeting. With the death of eight trustees over the previous decades and the recent resignation of five others, only four trustees remained. Under the Rules and Regulations of the Infirmary, which were redrawn in 1841, there was an obligation to ensure that when their number was reduced to eight, others would be appointed to bring their total up to 17 and thus form a full Board of Trustees. Duly invested, the new Board of Trustees of 1871 now sought changes 'in the system of the Institution', which resulted in two members of the medical staff resigning their positions. Replaced by 'a properly qualified practitioner, who had recently come to reside in the Town' there was also an unnamed 'Nurse' who, by the end of the year, was reported as having 'efficiently discharged her duties.[40]

Upon Matron Robinson's resignation in 1869, the names of the Matrons were no longer printed on the front page of the Infirmary's Annual General Meeting (AGM) Reports. That their exclusion followed the founding of the Nightingale Training School for Nurses in 1860 may have been a recognition that the Matrons of Bridgnorth's medical charity were 'untrained' nurses, and therefore could not be ascribed the title of 'Matron' for fear of embarrassment.

Following the amalgamation of the Infirmary with the Dispensary in January 1871, a chain of events occurred that related to Matron Martha Cheese. According to a minute of 2 December 1870, the 'Matron' was to receive notice and cease her employment at the end of that year. What actually happened is unclear, but from the 1871 AGM expenditure column a Matron is identified as receiving a salary of £10, in full, to 31 December 1870. The following line then identifies a Matron as being paid, in full, the sum of £50 'for 1871 (12 months)'. The next line then gives a Mrs Sutherland being paid 'Wages' of £22 15s 'during Matron's absence at St John's Hospital, London' during which time, Mrs Sutherland is described as 'Matron of House' (hence her inclusion in Table 3). Who was this Matron who was sent for training and which St John's Hospital had she attended? (as there were several by that name in nineteenth-century London). Again, uncertainty exists, but on the night of 2 April 1871 in the Parish of St Clement Danes, Strand, London, Martha Cheese is identified as being resident at Numbers 7 and 8 Norfolk Street. Described as a 'Nurse', aged 46 and born in Bridgnorth, Shropshire, her surname was given as 'Cheeze'.

At that time the buildings of Nos. 6, 7 and 8 Norfolk Street were leased to St John's House Training Institution for Nurses in St Clement Danes, Strand. With a connection established to St John's House, a search to place Martha Cheese in the Institution through the Registers of Probationers and Nurses ultimately failed due to a lack of surviving records.[41] However, in the Infirmary's revenue accounts of 1872, a 'Mrs Cheese, Matron' is identified. Thereafter there is no further mention of her name but her apparent successor was a 'Mrs Jones, Matron' who was first mentioned in 1874. It is therefore assumed that Martha Cheese was the unnamed 'Nurse' in the 1871 AGM Report, and that she ceased her employment as Matron in 1874 when the Matron's salary was given as £60 for that year.

That 'the Nurse' is cited in the 1871 AGM Report acknowledges, in part, her improved nursing status. However, there was also a need on the part of the Infirmary's committee to explain their 'exceptional expenditure of nearly £35' to the subscribers, particularly as they had spent £12 for the six months 'admission and training' of the Matron at St John's House that left an outstanding sum of £18 14s over income to be explained.

St John's House, which was founded in 1848 by an Anglican High Church group, began the training of women as nurses 12 years before Miss Nightingale introduced her training scheme in 1860. As an institution it provided domiciliary nurses to care for the sick in their own homes whilst taking over the nursing at two London hospitals: namely King's College Hospital (1856) and Charing Cross Hospital (1866).[42] The purpose of St John's House and the Anglican sisterhood who controlled the lay nurses was:

> To improve the qualifications and raise the character of Nurses for the sick, by
> providing for them professional training together with moral and religious discipline
> under the care of a clergyman, aided by the influence and example of a Lady
> Superintendent and other resident Sisters.[43]

Why Martha Cheese apparently ceased her employment in 1874 is not recorded. Similarly, there is no information about the dates on which Mrs Jones commenced or terminated her employment, other than that she appears to have departed some time in 1876. From the AGM Revenue Accounts for 1876, Matrons (plural) are identified as receiving £50 17s for the year, when a Mrs Thomas was apparently engaged as Matron to the Infirmary. Positively identified as being in post in 1877,[44] Mrs Harriet Thomas was aged about 50 years upon her appointment and married to John, some seven years her senior, who undertook the role of porter at the Infirmary.

Engaged initially on an annual salary of £30, Mrs Thomas served for nine years, receiving a salary increase of £5 during 1880 and a further £5 in 1883 when the annual sum of £40 included an allowance for night nursing, as and when serious cases arose. In these circumstances, Mrs Thomas was expected to engage an 'outside nurse', but apparently the task fell to her husband who 'was appointed as a night nurse, and so he acted, even to female patients in some instances', thereby saving the committee further expenditure – or so it was alleged.[45] Described as the 'Infirmary Nurse', by the summer of 1885 Mrs Thomas was no longer able to perform her duties and, being deemed 'past her art', she resigned with 'a present of £20 being given to her in recognition of her long service'.

The opportunity now existed for the Infirmary Committee to engage 'a Matron of a higher class, who should be a trained Nurse'; and so it came to pass that a 'trained nurse' was employed which resulted, once more, in the name of the Matron being reinstated upon the front page of the Infirmary's AGM Reports. Her appointment also initiated the modernisation of the Infirmary's fabric, which was in dire need of attention; but would the subscribers, some of whom seemed unaware of the advances that had taken place in medicine, nursing and hospital design, agree to such a programme? Determined to press ahead, the administrators of the Infirmary ventured forth only to discover that the concept of change would not be without its opponents!

5   CHANGE AND CONTINUITY

… When one considered the public spirit which always had breathed in the town of Bridgnorth and neighbourhood, he could not think for a moment that that meeting would allow the opportunity to pass without doing something towards starting a new institution. (Hear, hear.) The sentence in the report which referred to this matter was a very important one. The committee stated that with the small number of beds at their disposal, any further increase in the numbers of inpatients would place them in an embarrassed position; therefore, if the public really wished the benefits of the institution to be extended, if they wished to make more of the means already in hand, he was quite certain that it would be to the advantage of all persons concerned that some steps should be taken towards the erection of a new building (Hear, hear) …

A reported speech (part) by the Bishop of Hereford, 31 January 1890

T HE major changes that commenced in 1885 were primarily concerned with enhancing the efficiency of an institution that was both dirty and inadequate for its purpose.

There was also an appreciation, by some committee members, that considerable change had occurred in the wider world of hospital medicine where 'medical science [and] surgical science had not been standing still'.[1] This perceptive remark by a trustee was a recognition that medical men, who were now a distinct professional class, had entered an era of 'scientific medicine' that was heralded four decades earlier by the introduction of anaesthetic gases. Pioneered by James Young Simpson (1811–70) of Edinburgh, anaesthesia was now routinely administered to alleviate the pain previously endured by patients undergoing a surgical operation. The practice, however, was not without risk, as a local newspaper report of 1894 identified with the caption: 'Death under Chloroform'.[2]

Another complication of surgery, that was also life-threatening, was post-operative infection or the dreaded 'hospital gangrene'. It was a phenomenon that had exercised the mind of Joseph Lister (1827–1912) of Glasgow who was concerned with the post-operative mortality rates of his patients. Influenced by the 'beautiful researches' of Louis Pasteur (1822–96) and in the belief that germs might be the cause of infection and therefore putrefaction, Lister pioneered the use of carbolic acid (phenol), an antiseptic, during his surgical procedures, resulting in a significant reduction in his post-operative mortality rates. By the 1880s, those surgeons who ascribed to the 'Listerian' antiseptic – and later aseptic – surgical technique were also achieving success in their fight against post-operative infection.[3] Associated with these advances was the concept of 'germ theory' and the belief that germs caused disease. It was a view that was not widely held by the medical profession until the late 1890s, by which time Robert Koch (1843–1910) and his followers had proved conclusively that specific micro-organisms were responsible for certain diseases, including erysipelas[4] (confusingly also known as 'hospital gangrene' in the nineteenth century). Recognised today as classic cellulitis, a streptococcal infection, erysipelas was associated with 'hospitalism', a term introduced by Simpson and later defined by the surgeon, Sir John Erichsen (1818–96) as: '"a general morbid condition of the building, or of its atmosphere, productive of disease", in which patients got erysipelas and other contagions'.[5] Dreaded by hospital administrators, doctors, nurses and patients alike, erysipelas and 'hospitalism' would be a brief subject of discussion at the Bridgnorth Infirmary's annual meeting in 1891.

There was also an awareness that nursing had evolved, for it too had reformed and was striving to become 'professional' when the fight for statutory registration commenced in the 1880s. Such a change in nursing's fortunes was related, in part, to developments in nurse training and the realisation that such training improved the efficiency of hospitals. Added to this dimension was the fact that increasing numbers of middle-class women had joined the ranks of 'ladies' to become trained Hospital Nurses, where their structured education was now in schools of nursing located throughout the country in major teaching hospitals. Adept at managing households, their acquired nursing knowledge and practical skills had become a valued asset to the medical fraternity:

> *None, probably but medical men ... can guess how many lives are*
> *lost by bad and inefficient nursing, or the saving of health which one*
> *thoroughly trained Nurse can effect.*[6]

Related to all these developments was the concept of the modern hospital that included improved sanitary arrangements, ventilation and operating rooms fit for purpose. Such advances required the employment of another professional class in the planning and design of hospitals: the hospital architect, who also had to consider developments in hospital nursing. With the employment of increasing numbers of women, who were obliged to 'live-in', the introduction of separate, purpose-built accommodation occurred from the 1880s onwards at large institutions, where such buildings were known as the 'nurses' home'.[7]

Many of these developments, long in the making, were sadly lacking at the Bridgnorth Infirmary. A recognised problem was the ageing and untrained Infirmary Nurse, Mrs Thomas, who, by 1883, was incapable of managing the institution. It had been observed that there was 'a great untidiness throughout the Infirmary' which was compounded by the 'extremely disagreeable odour [that] arose from the dirty clothes of the patients' which were placed on the floor under the beds; hence the introduction of patients' lockers in 1885 to contain such smelly items. 'Bedsteads' were also said to be 'swarming with vermin' and the committee, unable to sell them on, chose to burn them. Meanwhile the patients, who were covered by 'one thin worn blanket to each bed', had 'little food', as it was alleged that Mrs Thomas 'chose to make a profit' by rationing their food supply. It was also stated that the bed of one patient had not been made for nine days, and if proof were needed then that person could be summoned to give their account.[8]

As for the overall state of the Infirmary, an undated minute reveals that in early 1885 the Infirmary:

> ... was in an unsatisfactory and unsanitary condition. The Matron was no longer able to do her work properly; the bedsteads were extremely uncomfortable; the bedding was insufficient and worn; the bedsteads, bedding, floor and walls were very dirty; the bathrooms were practically useless, as it took four hours to heat the baths; there were only three wards available for patients so that when the Institution was full one of the female patients had to share the servant's bed; there was no place in which to keep the linen or patients clothes; there was no waiting-room for out-patients; one of the largest and best rooms in the House was used as a Dispensary; all the washing had to be done inside the House, which is a very unsuitable arrangement in a Hospital; the system of ventilation and the Sanitary arrangements were bad and defective; many small repairs and a considerable amount of re-painting were needed in all parts of the Building; the garden was in an extremely untidy state; and the long flight of steps by which the Institution was approached was often a cause of great suffering to those who had received serious accidents.[9]

This neglected building and the management of it required addressing. The Infirmary Committee therefore took the decision, in 1883, to inform the subscribers that 'the services of a trained Hospital Nurse' would be secured in the autumn of 1884. However, such an appointment was dependent on payments from increased numbers of subscribers and particularly Provident Members, whose numbers were increasing.[10]

Membership of the Infirmary's Provident scheme (later known as the Bridgnorth Provident Society) entitled the working poor to put money aside on a monthly basis towards medical attention as an in-patient but not as an out-patient. The scheme therefore encouraged 'thrift' whilst making provision for any future illness. Inevitably, conditions were attached, including regarding those who were 'eligible' to participate. Thus, those members without children, whose wages did not exceed 20s per week, or those members with children, whose wages did not exceed 25s per week, were permitted to contribute, as per the scale of charges set out in Table 4.

Table 4. Monthly charges for Provident Members, 1883

Category	Charge per month
Persons over 16 years	5 pence
Man and Wife	8 pence
Widow, or Wives of Members of Friendly Societies	3 pence
Each child	2 pence
Child of a Widow	1 penny

N.B.	Children can only join with a parent, and until they are 16 years of age. Not more than 3 children will be charged for in one family.

Source: Bridgnorth Hospital Records: Report of the Committee for 1883

Monies derived from this scheme provided the Infirmary's administrators with a regular, if modest, income that in 1884 amounted to £23 19s 1d. A sum that, presumably, was insufficient to defray the expenditure of employing a 'trained Hospital Nurse', as an appointment did not occur in that year.

In the following year of 1885 Provident membership numbered 347, as opposed to 239 in the previous year, which brought in a sum of £36 18s 6d. Assured of a regular income (except, it was said, in those years when the town was deemed to be healthy by its poorer inhabitants), the Committee decided to appoint 'a Matron of a higher class' later in the year.

Prior to announcing this decision, the Committee sought to improve its efficiency at the beginning of 1885. To that end the General Committee of Management, which previously had been the only administrative body, now delegated portions of their work to form three further committees: one for finance; one for the House, whose committee would be responsible for its 'modernisation'; and one for surgery that would report on in-patient and out-patient activity (which had grown substantially) and the work of any future nursing staff.

There was also an apparent desire to modernise the role of the visitor, and as a consequence ten 'Lady Visitors' were appointed, reflecting the increasing role of middle-class women in charitable work.

Following such administrative improvements, the Committee now placed an advertisement for a 'trained Hospital Nurse'. Candidates, who were reimbursed for their railway travel expenses, were duly interviewed and on 24 June 1885, Miss Frances ('Fanny') Hadfield was 'elected' to the post of Matron at the Bridgnorth Infirmary. Aged 31 years and originally hailing from Matlock, Derbyshire, Miss Hadfield had previously occupied the post of 'Head Nurse [or ward sister] for eight years in the large Derby County Infirmary'. This is considered to be the Derbyshire General Infirmary that was established in 1804. Rebuilt during 1891–94, Queen Victoria laid the foundation stone in 1891, leading to the Infirmary subsequently being renamed the Derbyshire Royal Infirmary, which remains its name to this day.[11]

Spurred on with its success in 'securing the services of Miss Hadfield', the General Committee then instructed the House Committee – on a date unspecified – to undertake the extensive refurbishment of the Infirmary and its grounds. The wards were now closed for six weeks whilst the 'repairs' took place, that would ultimately cost £451 5d.

The alterations to the House included the allocation of a bedroom and a separate sitting room for Miss Hadfield's sole use, that reflected her standing as a trained nurse, and therefore her social status within the institution. Apart from providing appropriate accommodation for the Matron, there was also a pressing need to provide more beds. Hence the allocation of the 'Old Matron's bedroom', on the second floor, that was 'furnished as Ward No. 1', which suggests that the existing eight beds were supplemented by three additional beds to form a fourth ward.

A new bath, heated by gas, which could be 'made ready in less than 20 minutes', was also installed in one of the two closets on the second floor. The other closet was also 'fitted up with sink and shelves as a Matron's scullery for the washing of dressings etc', which suggests that clean, if not antiseptic techniques were to be introduced in the care and dressing of wounds. Although there is no mention of Miss Hadfield making up dressings (which was a time-consuming task undertaken by nurses) it is assumed that she not only made dressings but also washed them in addition to her other responsibilities, thereby increasing her workload. From an historical perspective, single-use dressings were introduced in the 1860s and made by nurses from either tow, cotton wool or lint, which, following one application, were then destroyed. Ultimately, this new practice replaced the use of the sponge and: 'the old routine of the surgeon going down the ward from patient to patient with one sponge and one basin of water'.[12]

Employed to manage the housekeeping and to nurse both the in-patients and the out-patients, which entailed visiting patients in their dwellings, Miss Hadfield was reported as having:

proved a most valuable acquisition to the Infirmary. She has thrown herself into
the work with her whole heart and soul and by her care and skill has materially
contributed to the recovery of several severe cases which could not have been
successfully treated without her aid.[13]

She had also adopted an improved system of housekeeping, that enabled the patients
to be better fed at a reduced cost, resulting in 'the average monthly expenditure on
nursing and maintenance [of patients being] actually less than it was before her time'.[14]

The negative side of all these improvements, including the day-to-day running of
the Infirmary where additional beds were now in use, was the recognised fact that:

All the staff have already felt the strain of over-work, and the servant, whose
conscientious work deserves grateful recognition, has suffered severely.[15]

To ameliorate this situation a 'charwoman' was engaged, who also undertook washing; but in the following year of 1886 a second servant was employed to assist with
the ever-increasing workload. All would have come under the supervision of Matron
Hadfield, who was paid an allowance for the board of the two servants in addition to
her annual salary, which, upon commencement of her employment, was £60.

The work of Miss Hadfield was also gaining momentum, as in 1886 she undertook
151 domiciliary visits to out-patients, under the direction of the medical staff. It was
a year in which 'Zymotic Diseases' proliferated amongst the out-patients, including outbreaks of whooping cough, measles and mumps, and seven cases of scarlet
fever and five cases of typhoid (none of which proved fatal). It was also a year in
which gifts of shrubs were donated for the garden, in preparation, perhaps, for the
arrival of the Bishop of Hereford, Dr Atlay. Arriving on 24 March 1886, the Bishop
was conducted over the Infirmary by the House Committee, which reported that
he had been 'pleased with everything that he has seen'. The Bishop, who accepted
the office of Visitor to the Infirmary in 1888, was supportive of those who appreciated the urgent need for a new infirmary building. In order to further their aim, he
accepted an invitation to preside over the annual general meeting of 1890, at which
he addressed the public on what was already a contentious issue – the desirability of
building a new infirmary.

Another issue that proved controversial was the appointment of an 'Assistant
Nurse' by the name of Miss Annie L. Banks. Elected to the post in the latter part
of 1887, Miss Banks was to receive an annual salary of £42 15s, that would include an
allowance for her board. Required to 'live-in', she was provided with a newly furnished room, that must previously have been used as a ward as bed numbers were later
said to be nine in total, a spare bed being set up in one of the wards.

The appointment of the Assistant Nurse was prompted by the illness of Matron Hadfield, who was to fall ill again in early 1891. Since commencing her duties in June 1885 there had been:

> an increase of more than 50 per cent in the number of in-patients in less than two years [that] had thrown a large amount of work upon the Matron, and her strength had been severely overtaxed.[16]

The Committee, drawn to the 'insufficiencies of the nursing arrangements' and other deficiencies in the House, responded with the 'permanent' appointment of the Assistant Nurse, which suggests that Miss Banks was employed as the temporary nurse during Matron's absence. The kitchen range, previously installed in 1885, was replaced, whilst a 'heating apparatus, including a new cistern [to] supply hot and cold water throughout the House', was installed in the expectation that it would 'save labour'.

These items, including new furniture and repairs, the employment of the temporary nurse, the triennial cleaning of the walls and ceilings of the Infirmary and the increased price of coal, incurred an expenditure of £650 4s 1d for the year of 1887. In this year Matron Hadfield's annual salary was now £75, with an allowance of £70 for her board and that of two servants.

As salaries, including that of the house-surgeon, were the 'principal' cause of increased costs representing 51 per cent of the Infirmary's income, the subscribers, perhaps not unreasonably, questioned the appointment of the Assistant Nurse. In response, it was stated that savings would be made, as the services of a night nurse would no longer be required (which, in 1887, had incurred an expenditure of £14). In the following year of 1888, when the question of the Assistant Nurse's employment and therefore her salary arose yet again, the Committee made it clear that 'the work of the Infirmary had so greatly increased' that her presence was necessary. They reiterated that her engagement avoided the need for a night nurse, who came from a distance, and was therefore 'procured at a very heavy cost'. Furthermore, both the Matron and the Assistant Nurse provided the patients with 'skilled nursing by night as well as by day'. They had also undertaken 286 domiciliary visits during the year, which not only 'greatly assisted' the house-surgeon but also 'helped to inculcate habits of cleanliness amongst the out patients';[17] a duty for which the nurses were publicly thanked by the Honorary Surgeon, Dr William Rhodes.

If salaries were a concern to the subscribers in 1887, so too was the question of how income might be enhanced, particularly as the locality was affected by a 'depression in trade and agriculture' (as was being experienced elsewhere at that time). One subscriber made the suggestion that the Infirmary was unlikely to get any more money unless the Committee 'extended their sphere of operation'. In reply, it was stated that, although two infirmaries existed in the county at Shrewsbury and Oswestry, the Infirmary was doing all the work between Bridgnorth and Ludlow, where a cottage hospital had been established in the Old College Buildings during the latter part of 1884.[18]

Meanwhile the Infirmary Committee, ever alert to the fluctuating economic and social conditions of the day, had introduced a scheme to raise more money, which was met with disapproval amongst some subscribers. This was the introduction of

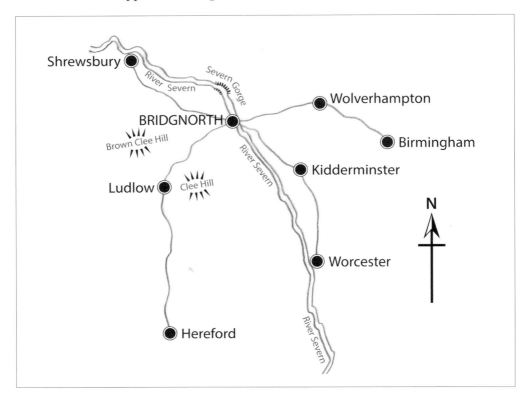

TOWNS ASSOCIATED WITH THE BRIDGNORTH INFIRMARY IN THE NINETEENTH CENTURY (*not to scale*)

Shrewsbury: The Salop Infirmary received patients from Bridgnorth and district.
Worcester: Dr Jonas Malden, Consultant Physician to the Infirmary, appointed 1835.
Kidderminster: Advertisement for a Matron in the *Ten Town's Messenger*, 1841.
Birmingham: Dr Bell Fletcher, Consulting Physician to the Infirmary, *c*.1842.
Wolverhampton: Dr Topham, Consulting Physician to the Infirmary, *c*.1850.
Ludlow: Rural district between Bridgnorth and Ludlow covered by the Infirmary until 1884, when a cottage hospital was opened in Ludlow.
Hereford: The Bishops of Hereford were appointed as Visitors to the Bridgnorth Infirmary, as it was situated (and remains so) within the Diocese of Hereford.

the 'well-to-do-classes' as fee-paying patients, which, by implication, was perceived as denying the poorer classes access to the Infirmary's facilities. This suggestion was rejected, with the explanation that fee-paying patients were being admitted, but only 'when there was room' at the Infirmary.

All these changes, including those that had occurred since 1885, now brought forth the criticism that members of the Infirmary Committee were changing the character of the institution and that these changes were not consistent with the original intensions of its founders. However, there was one further change that the subscribers were willing to accept, which was a change in the name of the institution.

At a special meeting, held on 25 November 1887, the Infirmary Committee unanimously resolved:

> That it is desirable that the name of this Institution be changed to The Bridgnorth and South Shropshire Infirmary.[19]

The reasons given to the subscribers for the name change, which they were encouraged to view as an addition rather than an alteration and therefore approve, were that:

> the Bridgnorth Infirmary was the oldest and most important in the South Shropshire district, and that, at present, the name Bridgnorth Infirmary often conveyed to new residents in the district the idea that the benefits were confined to Bridgnorth alone;

> it was usual for an institution like the Infirmary to have a name representative of the district from which it received patients and subscriptions.

Furthermore, such a change in the name would alert the residents of the County to its existence and therefore lead to greater interest in the establishment.[20] The aim, therefore, was to increase the Infirmary's subscription list, as subscriptions were the 'mainstay' of the institution, where increasing demands on finite resources were a constant concern to the administrators.

Meanwhile, the house-surgeon Dr Horace Jefferies (or Jeffries), who had been appointed on 19 January 1885, had also contributed to the efficiency of the House by keeping all the books so accurately that they formed 'a complete record of work at the Institution', which apparently had not been the case in previous years.[21]

This popular doctor eventually resigned his post in the early summer months of 1887 as he had purchased a private medical practice in Bolton. His successor was a Mr G.A. Holroyd, whose previous employment had been that of 'assistant surgeon at the Derby Infirmary'. This raises the question: did Matron Hadfield remain in contact with colleagues at her previous workplace?

If she did, so too did Dr Jefferies, as he was to return to Bridgnorth on two separate occasions: the first being on Wednesday, 26 October 1887, when he was presented with a gift 'by a few of his grateful patients'. In giving thanks, Dr Jefferies spoke of his time at the Infirmary, which had 'certainly been the happiest of his life'. He also paid tribute to Matron Hadfield, stating 'that half of [his] success had been due to her exertions, and he took the opportunity to acknowledge his thanks for her help towards his patients'. He also added that since being at his practice in Bolton he found it 'very different from the quiet of the Infirmary'[22] where, at the end of 1887 there had been a 'continued increase in every part of the house-surgeon's work'.[23]

Whether or not the increased workload had affected Mr Holroyd's health is unrecorded, but in early 1888 he fell ill for 'several weeks' and was 'eventually obliged to resign'. During his absence a *locum tenens* – a temporary doctor – was engaged; however, it was Matron Hadfield who undertook 'a good deal of the house-surgeon's work' until a Mr Frederick Maurice House, MRCS, LRCP was appointed on 29 May 1888. At the close of that year in-patients were recorded as 82 persons, with an average length of stay of 21.2 days, and a death rate, of whole numbers under treatment, of 2.54 per cent. With the Infirmary stretched to capacity, the Committee now publicly announced, for the first time, that it would 'shortly become necessary to build a new Infirmary', where a larger number of patients could be attended in a more convenient building.[24]

This declaration was repeated by the Infirmary Committee in the following year of 1889 and reinforced by the House Committee, who reported that:

> *During the year the House Committee have not found it necessary to recommend the execution of any important structural works. Such minor repairs as have been needed have been done, but the floors throughout the Institution are so much worn that it is no longer possible to repair them in a satisfactory manner, and it seems scarcely worth while to undertake such expensive work as the renewal of all the floors of a building which is, in many respects, very unsuitable for a hospital, and which is built on a site which is very inconvenient, if there is any prospect of a new Hospital on a more convenient site. In such a building a much larger amount of work might be done without over-taxing the strength of the present staff.*[25]

The subscribers, unmoved by the difficulties now facing the administrators, rejected the need for a new infirmary as, in their view, there had already been a considerable expenditure on the existing building. Undaunted, the committee members now sought to place the issue firmly on the agenda, and in the intervening months they turned to the Infirmary's distinguished Visitor, the Bishop of Hereford, to assist them in their endeavours. The Bishop, as previously mentioned, agreed to preside over the next annual general meeting, that took place in the Town Hall on 31 January 1890.

In his address[26] the Bishop spoke without 'any bias in his mind' on what he had seen earlier that day. As to the state of the Infirmary, 'a cleaner place he was never in' but alas the mortuary (which was situated in the cave) 'was absolutely unworthy of being for any time the receptacle of a dead body – of a body that had been the Temple of the Holy Spirit'. Similarly, the operating room 'was quite unfit for the purposes for which it was used', whilst the 'locality' and the 'terrible steps' were sufficient reasons in themselves for asking for a new building. The inadequate number of beds was also a concern for 'any further increase in the numbers of in-patients would place [the committee] in an embarrassed position'. Therefore, in the opinion of the Bishop, 'it was absolutely necessary that a new Infirmary should be erected': a phrase that he had previously uttered in his speech and one that would be questioned – together with the authority of the Bishop – in the following year of 1891.

The Town Hall, which had been restored and refurbished in 1888 to mark Queen Victoria's Golden Jubilee in the previous year, was the venue for public meetings. It was here, in December 1890, that the Bridgnorth Medical Aid Association was founded by four laymen[27] who had previously 'thrashed out' the preliminaries with the Infirmary Committee. The scheme, which was open to all persons whose wages did not exceed £2 2s per week, did not require a medical examination prior to entering, and permitted each member to choose their own general practitioner (GP), thus bringing 'medical aid to the doors of the working poor'. The aim was to remove not only the stigma of being 'an object of charity' when seeking out an Infirmary ticket as an out-patient, but also to alleviate 'the nightmare of a big bill from the doctor', that would unnecessarily 'impede the patient's recovery'. It was therefore suggested that:

> It was better for every person in the town to join such an Association than to go begging for Infirmary notes or spending a lot of money in quack medicine when they could get the very best advice in this town for a few shillings a year.[28]

The 'very best advice' was to come from three general medical practitioners, all of whom were honorary surgeons at the Bridgnorth Infirmary. Of the three, the most senior in age (52 years) and rank was the highly qualified Dr William Thursfield, junior, LRCP (Lon); MRCS (Eng); MD (Aberd); DPH who lived at No. 39, High Street. Born in Bridgnorth into a medical family, he was a justice of the peace (JP), a Surgeon to the 1st Voluntary Battalion, Kings Shropshire Light Infantry (KSLI) and Medical Officer of Health (MOH, public health) not only to the Bridgnorth Rural District Council but also, in 1890, to the Shropshire County Council as the County's first public health medical officer (a post that would become full-time in 1897).[29]

Second was Mr Alfred Bethell, MRCS (Eng), a native of Somerset who, aged

40, resided at No. 22 East Castle Street and whose professional relationship with Dr Thursfield was strained.[30] As the Medical Officer of Health (MOH, public health) for the Borough of Bridgnorth, Bethell was expected, amongst other things, to contain epidemics in the town and provide Thursfield, and indeed the Medical Aid Association, with statistical data. Inexplicably, he was unable to do either effectively or efficiently. However, it did not prevent Bethell from becoming the MOH for the Rural Sanitary District in 1897 on an annual salary of £40 and, like many medical men who experienced financial uncertainty in general practice, Bethell also undertook additional paid work to supplement his income as a Certifying Factory Surgeon. In 1899 he became an Honorary Consulting Surgeon to the Infirmary; an appointment that was made in appreciation of his past services to the institution.

The third and youngest of the trio, at 37 years, was Dr William Rhodes, LRCP, LLM (Edin), MRCS (Eng), who was appointed as an honorary staff member to the Infirmary in 1882. Resident at North Gate House, No. 7 High Street, he, like Thursfield, was a JP and a supporter of the Infirmary's Honorary Secretary, the Revd John P. Wright and others, in promoting the need for a new infirmary building.

Two months later, on the afternoon of Tuesday 3 February 1891, the Infirmary Committee held their annual general meeting in the Town Hall, where a series of exchanges, primarily between the Revd John P. Wright and Mr Bethell, erupted to create 'A Stormy Meeting'. From the extensive report in the *Bridgnorth Journal*[31] there is an impression that Bethell was an opinionated man who saw little reason to attend Infirmary meetings, thereby excluding himself from various committees, including the House Committee, and 'being a particularly modest man he didn't like being snubbed'. He also considered that the Bishop's visit and subsequent speech was a 'farce [that] had been played out', which brought forth the comment from the floor that Bethell had 'exceeded the limits of debate in suggesting how the opinion expressed by the Bishop was formed'.

Bethell was also aggrieved that he had not been consulted on the state of the Infirmary, for if a building were to be condemned then he, as MOH, should have been approached; and as he was not he thought he had been 'treated with very scant courtesy'. Concerning the Infirmary's structural defects, Bethell suggested that the house-surgeon's damp bedroom could be rectified by further excavations and the use of concrete; but excavation and previous works to remedy the problem had proved unsatisfactory. With regard to the worn floorboards, they could be boarded over and made perfectly good; however, pieces of tin were already in place, and boarding over was not an option as it had been 'tried at Derby', where such a scheme had failed to work. As for the mortuary, all that was required was an expenditure of some £15–£20 to enable it to 'be made all that was desired'.

Nor did Mr Bethell consider the Infirmary to be in a 'diseased condition' – a reference to 'hospitalism' – although he acknowledged that two cases of erysipelas had previously been 'admitted' to the institution. However, as Dr Rhodes exclaimed: 'Were they to wait until they [the Infirmary] got disease or were they to say they did not believe the present Infirmary was fitted to the work?' Dr Rhodes also stated that the cubic space per patient was 'far below what was considered necessary for hospital patients', which was later said to be 700 cubic feet per patient at the Infirmary as opposed to the then current minimum standard of 1,200 cubic feet.[32]

Continuing in a desultory manner, Bethell also opined that the recently formed Bridgnorth Medical Aid Association might be injurious to the Infirmary's Provident scheme, which was flourishing. Asked by the Revd Wright to speak out plainly, Bethel responded with the comment that 'the continuance of the Provident Branch was unfair to the Medical men of the town'. Here was another grievance, as the monies raised by the Provident scheme went to the Infirmary and not into the pockets of the medical men – unlike the newly formed Medical Aid Association, where fees, set by the medical men, were received for services rendered. It was an issue that would be raised again in 1898 when Dr Thursfield 'regretted' that the Provident scheme had not been abolished so that only one Medical Association existed in the town. However, as Mr Alfred Stringer Trevor, an Infirmary trustee who was also the Borough Treasurer, suggested: 'moderate competition' was appropriate, as 'choice' was provided by the existence of the two schemes, particularly as those patients attending the Infirmary no longer had to beg for 'letters' and where neither institution had a need to employ a 'half-fledged medico'.[33]

Of the many opinions expressed by Mr Bethell, one which had a particular resonance with others was the question of how money would be raised for a new infirmary. Acknowledging that a new infirmary would be an advantage to all concerned, Bethell suggested three ways of raising funds; first 'was the hope that some good fairy would drop some three to four thousand pounds into the Treasurer's hands and say "Build"'; second was the selling of vested stock, that he and others were firmly against, and third was an appeal to the town and neighbourhood for funds. Upon the latter, Bethell was not optimistic, as he had spoken to 'one of the Infirmary's largest benefactors' who had informed him that:

> I don't think you in the town can find £4,000 and in the immediate neighbourhood the country gentlemen have to support so many Institutions that they are not in a position that would enable them to help you to any great extent.

Finally, the AGM came to a close with an agreement that the present building should be kept in 'a state of repair', and if funds could be raised towards a new infirmary then that would be 'a step in the right direction'.

The initiative was now taken by Mr T. Martin Southwell, Infirmary Trustee and Managing Director of the family business H&M Southwell Ltd., carpet manufacturers of Bridgnorth (1809–1944),[34] who initiated a Dolleries Bazaar. Organised and run by the women of Bridgnorth's 'great and good', the bazaar was primarily an exhibition and sale of dolls alongside stalls and other activities that was held in the Agriculture Hall on 16 December 1891. The monies raised, including smaller collections in the year, amounted to £203 19s 11d, to which was added a bequest of £100, thus enabling a Building Fund to be established.

The next step was to find a convenient site within the confines of the town that would be suitable for a new building. The search would come to fruition in 1892, when Mr T. Martin Southwell provided further practical support by offering 'about one acre' of land, or its professionally determined value of £300, as a site for the new infirmary. Although the land, which was situated to the east of North Gate, had certain disadvantages, including a 'difficult approach', the offer was gratefully accepted. However, reservations about the site's location must have existed as two years later an alternative site was offered and accepted with alacrity.

'North Gate, Bridgnorth'. A pencil study on paper by Henry Harris Lines (1801–1889) that was probably made between 1818 and 1829 and measuring 265 x 190cm. Viewed from the north, note the buildings above the steps on the far right of the drawing where cottages once stood prior to 1894. Image credit: photo taken by Simon Bruntnell and provided by the Royal Birmingham Society of Artists.

Meanwhile, the year of 1892 was blighted by an agricultural depression and an outbreak of influenza that had been prevalent in the town since 1890. These 'severe epidemics of influenza' had abated by 1896 to 'a few light cases',[35] none of which was admitted to the Infirmary (where patients had been refused admission due, it was said, to a lack of beds not a policy of exclusion). This situation, some suggested, could be resolved by transporting patients by train to Shrewsbury for treatment at the Salop Infirmary. However, the notion was rejected with the argument that the journey would be too painful for the patients and too far for both relatives and medical men to visit, hence the need for a larger and more 'convenient house' with additional beds that would meet the needs of patients and staff. As for the problem of the house-surgeon's damp bedroom, that too was addressed in 1892 when further building works were undertaken to rectify the dampness that was then 'believed cured'.[36]

A further and seemingly intractable problem for the Infirmary Committee members, nine of whom had formed a Building Committee, was the continuing unwillingness of the subscribers to formally approve fund-raising activities and a building scheme for a new infirmary. If uncertainty existed over this matter then the year of 1893 would bring unforeseen benefits, commencing on 1 February when the Infirmary Committee was informed by William Henry Foster, elder son of William Orme Foster, that his father would donate £1,000 to the building fund. Within a few days the Right Honourable Viscount Boyne of Burwarton had also followed suit with a donation of £400.[37] With a Building Fund of £1,703 19s 11d (representing 43 per cent of the estimated £4000 for a new build) the Infirmary committee drew up a 'Special Report' on the proposed infirmary, that was distributed to every subscriber, prior to the annual general meeting on 6 April 1893.

It was at this meeting that, for the first time in five years, the committee now obtained what they required: a resolution, passed unanimously, that empowered them 'to prepare a scheme and solicit subscriptions' for a new infirmary. With their patience rewarded, it now fell to the Building Committee to raise further monies and search out an architect who, ultimately, would be responsible for the design and build of the new Infirmary.

There was, as there had been 61 years earlier, much work to be done by a dedicated few that on this occasion included Mr F.W. Hewett (Hon. Treasurer), the Revd John P. Wright (Hon. Secretary) and the Revd E. Elliott (Assistant Hon. Secretary), all of whom were described as 'experiencing perhaps the greatest calls upon their energy'[38] in advancing the scheme for a new infirmary that would, to all intents and purposes, be 'of the age'.

6 FIT FOR THE AGE

Above the main entrance of the 1896 building there is a chronogram, crafted in yellow and green faience (glazed earthenware), which reflects the Victorian values of the Bridgnorth and South Shropshire Infirmary at its opening:

BENEFICIS CVRANTIBVS
AEGROTANTIBVS MORITVRIS
SIT IN CHRISTO PAX
GRATIA FIDES SALVS
MDCCCLXVVVVVVIIIIIIIIIIII

It is not easy to translate literally such a Latin inscription into well-sounding English, but the following rendering is accepted by the gentleman who composed the chronograph: 'To our Benefactors, to the Healers, to the Sick, and to the Dying, in Christ be Peace, Grace, Faith, and Salvation 1896'.

The *Bridgnorth Journal*, Saturday 19 September 1896

ALL augured well for the Infirmary Committee following the successful outcome of the annual meeting in April 1893. Empowered to raise subscriptions, the Committee launched an appeal for funds, which was 'liberally responded to',[1] enabling the Committee to pursue their next priority: securing the services of an architect through an architectural competition.

The process commenced in July when advice was sought from Mr Macvicar Anderson, President of the Royal Institute of British Architects (RIBA). This gentleman would subsequently appoint a professional assessor to assist the Committee in drawing up conditions for a competition and in the selection of the most suitable design from those submitted by the competing architects. Within months, 44 competing architects had responded with their plans, ten of whom were selected by the Building Committee for further consideration. Then, in November and upon the advice of the assessor Mr Alexander Graham, a Vice-President of the RIBA, the Committee 'approved of and accepted the plans' submitted by Mr Edward Charles Henry Maidman (1866–1918) of Edinburgh.[2]

Articled in 1884 to Mr William T. Hollands, FRIBA of London, Edward Maidman became an assistant at various architectural practices in Hastings and London before being appointed to Mr James Bow Dunn (1861–1930) of Edinburgh. Following his success in the competition, Maidman became an elected member of the Edinburgh Architectural Association and eventually one of its Vice-Presidents.[3] Described in the local press[4] as 'a rising young architect who is well known in Edinburgh', Maidman would eventually move to Bridgnorth and establish an office at No. 23 High Street from whence he would superintend the building of the new infirmary.

Following Mr Maidman's appointment there followed 'An Earnest Appeal from the Committee of the Bridgnorth and South Shropshire Infirmary for £1,000 … to complete the sum of £4,000 estimated as the cost of the new Building'.[5] Printed as a circular and dated December 1893, the appeal was primarily aimed at 'those inhabitants of Shropshire' who had yet to subscribe to the new venture. It was hoped by those concerned that there would be 'an early and favourable response' as the working drawings for the new infirmary, and therefore the building works, could not commence until all the monies were to hand: a stipulation that had been placed on the Infirmary Committee by the subscribers.

The appeal, however, brought little if any response from the county, as on 14 February 1894 a further 'urgent appeal' was published in the *Bridgnorth Journal* in which it was stated that monies already promised amounted to £2,972 7s 11d. If the response to the circular (presumably printed at some expense) had been disappointing, the Building Committee chose to press ahead, and requested Mr Maidman commence the working drawings that, in the following year, would require alterations and additions to enhance the efficiency and economy of the buildings.

Some five months later, and much to the delight of all concerned, a new development occurred that required immediate attention. On the evening of Tuesday 7 August 1894, the Building Committee convened a meeting to discuss an offer, from Mr William Orme Foster, of an alternative site for a new infirmary.[6] The land, which was a part of Mr Foster's Apley Estate, was situated to the west of North Gate, in an elevated position off the Broseley Road. The new site was 'almost immediately opposite' Mr T. Martin Southwell's site, which had a difficult approach and was 'out of sight of the high road'.[7] Several members of the Committee, including Mr Maidman, had visited the site that same afternoon. Maidman 'thought the new site an excellent one' as the approach would be more convenient, especially for the patients. Furthermore, the cost of making

'*Bridgnorth'. A general view of the town from Knowle Sands by Joseph Powell (1780–1834), first president of the New*
ciety of Painters in Water Colours (1832–1833). Dated 1832, the watercolour measures 12.75 inches x 8.5 inches.
ourtesy of Tony Rickards

The Bridgnorth Infirmary, 1836–1896. Designed on
onomic principles' and erected by Josiah Griffiths of
uatford during the latter part of 1835, the Infirmary
eived its first patients in February 1836.
ourtesy of Bob Waugh (photographed in 2001)

3. *North Gate House, 7 High Street, Bridgnorth. The*
residence of Dr Rhodes, which, in 1957, was adapted to house
the Bridgnorth Medical Practice when the town's general
practitioners combined their respective medical practices
to form one of the first group practices in the country. The
practice partners vacated the building for a purpose-built
primary health care centre in 2007.
Courtesy of the late Mr John Hares
(photographed in 1967)

4. *Miss Frances 'Fanny' Hadfield (1854–1927). An early undated photograph of Miss Hadfield while nursing in Derby. She became the Bridgnorth Infirmary's first 'trained hospital nurse' and 'Matron of a higher class'. Much respected, her tenure dated from June 1885 to December 1894.*
Courtesy of Mrs Barbara M. Loudon

5. *Dr William Rhodes, LRCP, MRCS, LM (Edin), (1853–1908). A physician and surgeon with a midwifery qualification, Dr Rhodes practised as a general practition in Bridgnorth where he was appointed as an honorary surgeon to the Infirmary in 1882. Actively involved in the town's affairs, he became a Justice of the Peace and Mayor Bridgnorth 1886–1887.*
Courtesy of Mrs Ann Kerr

6. *Bridgnorth Infirmary Staff 188 Matron Hadfield (front row, far right) with unidentified members of the medical and nursing staff in August 1889. Why this group photograph was taken is unknow however, in post in 1889 were the Assistant Nurse, Miss Annie L. Banks, the House-Surgeon, Mr Frederick M. House MRCS, LRCP, whilst the President of th renamed (1887) Bridgnorth and South Shropshire Infirmary was Captain T.C. Douglas Whitmore* Courtesy of The League of Friends of Bridgnorth Hospital

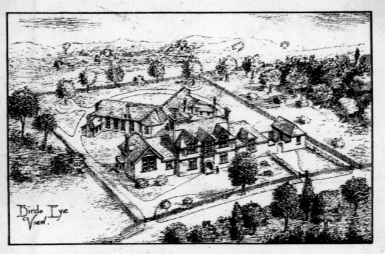

7. "'Tis Sixty Years Since".
This four-page circular dated
December 1893, was an 'earnest
appeal' to the inhabitants
of Shropshire for donations
towards the cost of erecting
the 'New Infirmary'. Also
encouraged within its pages
was the establishing of a
hospital bed IN MEMORIAM
of a relative or friend at a cost
of £125 to those of a 'charitable
disposition'.
Courtesy of the Manager
Bridgnorth Hospital

"'TIS SIXTY YEARS SINCE."

An Earnest Appeal from the Committee of the Bridgnorth and South Shropshire Infirmary for £1,000 still required to complete the sum of £4,000 estimated as the cost of the new Buildings.

December, 1893.

SIR WALTER SCOTT in writing his first novel gave to it the sub-title, "'Tis Sixty years since." Sixty years is a very short space of time in the history of a people, but there are even shorter periods which have been sufficient to bring about such great changes that to look back over them seems like taking a peep into ancient history. At the time of the publication of "Waverley," this was the case with the "Sixty years since," in which the events of that novel were supposed to have taken place.

8. The Opening of the New
Infirmary. An important
occasion and one of civic pride,
the Infirmary was opened by the
Viscountess Boyne of Burwarton
on Thursday, 17 September 1896
in 'pelting rain'.
Courtesy of The League
of Friends of Bridgnorth
Hospital

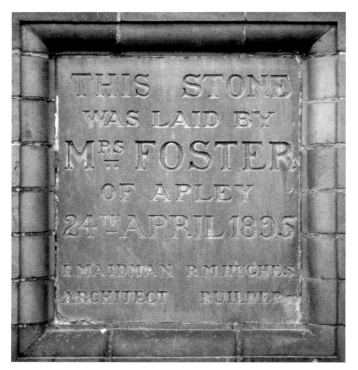

11. *The Commemorative Medal. A gift of the Mayor, Mr Edmund M. Southwell, which was presented to the children and adult members of Bridgnorth's Friendly Societies at the opening of the new infirmary.*

9. *The Foundation Stone of the Bridgnorth and South Shropshire Infirmary was laid by Mrs W.O. Foster of Apley Park on Wednesday, 24 April 1895. The architect, E.C.H. Maidman and the builder, R.M. Hughes of Birmingham are also acknowledged on the stone. Within the stone's cavity is that day's* London Times *and a copy of the* Bridgnorth Journal *for Saturday, 20 April 1895.* © Gillian Waugh Pead

The reverse of the Commemorative Medal shows a Bridgnorth Seal that was adopted by the Corporation in the nineteenth century as the Borough's 'Coat of Arms' with the transcribed motto: 'In the Town's loyalty lies the King's safety.'
Courtesy of Ann Chadwick

10. *Postcard of the Bridgnorth Infirmary from the James Valentine Series No. 26484. The title was first registered in 1897, but the exact date of the image is unknown. Note the flagpole upon which the Union Flag was flown when injured military personnel were in residence during WWI.* The major archive of monochrome topographical views by James Valentine and Sons is held by the University of St Andrews Library. For further details of this collection please contact the Library or refer to: http://www.st.-andrews.ac.uk/library/specialcollection

12. *Military patients at the Infirmary during the First World War. On 17 March 1915 the Infirmary officially became the Bridgnorth Infirmary Auxiliary Military Hospital when a ward was set aside for the reception of those wounded in the Battle of Neuve Chapelle (10–13 March 1915). During its Military status, 787 wounded army and naval personnel passed through its doors, until March 1919 when civilian status was resumed.* © Shropshire Archives XLS 2633; SA C21.3

13. *A ward during the First World War. A gas-lit ward at the Bridgnorth Infirmary Auxiliary Military Hospital c.1917 from a glass plate negative found by the late Mr R. Holden, assistant engineer at the Infirmary, during a 'spring-clean' in 1974. Note the nurse wearing a black arm band as a sign of mourning.* Courtesy of the *Bridgnorth Journal.* NB Mrs Holden, widow of the late Mr R. Holden, has no recollection of what became of the glass plate negatives discovered by her husband.

14. *The Lady Forester Convalescent Home, Llandudno, North Wales. Designed by architect Mr Edward Blakeway L'Anson and built by Messrs W. Brown and Son of Salford, the home was opened on 17 October 1904 to serve both private and charitable patients, including those of the Bridgnorth and South Shropshire Infirmary from 1905.*
Courtesy of The Lady Forester Trust

15. *The War Memorial, Bridgnorth. The 7' 6" (2.29m) figure of a British soldier was designed and worked by the Salopian sculptor, Captain Adrian Jones, MVO, RBS; cast in bronze by Mr A.B. Burton of Surrey and unveiled on 9 March 1922 by Private Eli Jones (unrelated to the sculptor), a disabled veteran of WWI and native of Bridgnorth. Situated in the Castle Grounds, the figure stands upon a 10' (3.5m) pedestal of Alveley stone that was worked by Mr Banks, stone mason of Bridgnorth.*
Photographer and date unknown. Author's collection

16. *Seal of the Shropshire Insurance Committee. Following the enactment of the National Insurance Act 1911 on 15 July 1912, Insurance Committees were required to have a Common Seal, and this image represents the Salop (Shropshire) Committee. The seal was designed by its chairman, Mr R. Lloyd Kenyon. The design depicts a hand holding a rod around which a serpent is coiled. The latter symbolises the Rod of Aesculapius, the ancient Greek god of medicine and healing, whilst the hand is adapted from the Seals of Shrewsbury and Buildwas Abbey, both of which had a hand holding a crozier. Above the design is a scroll containing the words: 'Venienti Occurrite Morbo' meaning 'Fight disease while it is approaching': a motto that, at that time, represented the principles of Insurance.*
Courtesy of Shropshire Archaeological and Historical Society

No..............   Children ....
Name..............   Doctor ....
Address ....   Contributions...........per quarter.

1922.	Contributions	Received by
March 25		
June 24		
Sept. 23		
Dec. 23		

1923.	Contributions	Received by
March 24		
June 23		
Sept. 22		
Dec. 22		

1924.	Contributions	Received by
March 22		
June 21		
Sept. 20		
Dec. 20		

1925.	Contributions	Received by
March 21		
June 20		
Sept. 19		
Dec. 19		

. Medical Aid Club Card. On 1 April 1914 Doctors Craig, Padwick and Dickson resigned as medical officers to the ~idgnorth Friendly Societies' Medical Association to commence their own Medical Aid club following the appointment of e two panel doctors Messrs Berry and Devonald to the Association. Shown here is the Medical Aid club card for the years 22–25 which bears the names of Doctors Craig, Rhodes and Dickson. Dr E.L.N. Rhodes replaced Dr Padwick whose signation prompted his departure from Bridgnorth.
ourtesy of the Trustees of the Bridgnorth and District Historical Society, Northgate Museum

The Midwives and Maternity Homes Act, 1926
PART II.

Certificate of Registration.

This is to Certify that the Salop County Council have registered the Committee of the Bridgnorth & South Shropshire Infirmary in respect of their Infirmary Maternity Home at Bridgnorth in accordance with the provisions of the above Act.

Dated this 27th day of February, 1928.

Signature ....

. Certificate of Registration. Maternity cases were excluded from the Infirmary until 1922, and is Certificate of Registration, dated 27 February 1928, required the Infirmary's administrators comply with The Midwives and Maternity Homes Act 1926 which was related to the gistration and general supervision of maternity homes by Local Authorities including the Salop ounty Council. Courtesy of the Manager Bridgnorth Hospital

If you're not well,
come to
Bridgnorth

19. *The Maternity Wing, photographed in 1993. The Maternity Wing was opened on Thursday, 27 September 1934 by the Marchioness of Cambridge, and erected by Messrs Lay and Son, builders of Bridgnorth, on land behind the Infirmary that had been donated by Major A.W. Foster, MC of Apley Park. The stone plaque, visible on the side of the building, read: 'This addition was erected by public subscription for maternity work. September 1934.' Neither the building nor the plaque has survived further developments at the Infirmary.*
© Crown Copyright NMR (AA021600)

20. *Come to Bridgnorth. Between the late nineteenth and early twentieth centuries Bridgnorth was perceived – and promoted – a health resort, as this postcard from the early 1900s demonstrates* Courtesy of Mrs M.R. Hamilton

21. *Bridgnorth and South Shropshire Infirmary Staff, 1934. Identified with Matron, Miss A.A. Taylor (front row, centre) at the opening of the maternity wing in September 1934 are (L–R): Acting Staff Nurse D. Withy; Midwifery Sister N. Parker; (Matron); Sister G.P. Robinson; and Assistant Nurse B. Roberts. Those in the back row include: Probationers M Hall; Weaver; Talbot; D. Pope; Lewis; and Brick.*
Courtesy of the Mapp family

an access road would also be reduced 'by at least one-half', as would any future mainte-nance. Although his plans had been drawn with the Southwell site in mind 'they fitted perfectly with that now suggested', particularly if the main administrative block was set 'some 30 yards back from the high road' as the building would be 'evidenced' from the highway; a consideration that was deemed important, especially as the institution was supported by public subscriptions. There was also a general agreement that the site was 'still nearer to the town' than the Southwell site and therefore a resolution was passed to abandon the former site for the Apley site. Instrumental in this decision was Mr Edmund M. Southwell, the second son of Mr T. Martin Southwell, who also proposed that the Apley site should be purchased 'forthwith' for the sum of £300.

There now followed a discussion on when building could commence, as Mrs Foster had already agreed to lay the foundation stone. The month of October was suggested; but, as the presiding chairman, Dr Rhodes, explained: 'actual possession could not be obtained until next March, unless with the consent of the tenants'. This was a reference to two tenanted Apley Estate cottages, Nos. 18 and 19 North Gate, that were included in the site. The tenant of No. 18 North Gate (with an orchard attached) was Mr Henry Wilmot (or Wilmott) and his family, who paid an annual rent of £8; whilst their neighbour, Elizabeth Stanton, paid an annual rent of £5 4s.[8] The cottages, which are depicted in a naive oil painting,[9] would subsequently be demolished to permit access to the site, the tenants having vacated their respec-tive dwellings by March 1895.

Finally, the meeting came to a close with the agreement that, as subscriptions had risen to £3,200 towards a revised total of £4,500, Mr Maidman should 'proceed immediately' with the new working plans. It was also agreed that tenders should be invited for either the execution of the whole work or the erection of part of it from the monies already subscribed. The decision was deferred until the following year as, on 6 October 1894, an unexpected event occurred when a wealthy widow in the town of Bromsgrove drew her last breath.[10] The deceased was Mrs Sarah Eliza Baker, a native of Morville, whose husband John Baker, once a Master of Foxhounds, had pre-deceased his wife 29 years earlier. During their respective lives each had subscribed to the Bridgnorth Infirmary, an association that had continued after Mrs Baker left the Bridgnorth area to reside elsewhere before settling in Bromsgrove.

A further association with the locality was provided by the two surviving execu-tors of her estate: Mr George Pudsey Aston Pudsey of Seisdon Hall, Staffordshire, who was a Vice-President and Trustee of the Infirmary, and fellow trustee, the previ-ously mentioned Mr Alfred Stringer Trevor of Sudely House, Bridgnorth. With Mrs Baker's fortune entrusted to these two gentlemen, and in accordance with her will, various bequests were made, including one to Morville School where, on 22 January 1896, an extension was opened and named the 'Baker' Infant School. Thereafter, Mrs

Numbers 18 and 19 North Gate, Bridgnorth. This naïve oil painting of the two Apley Estate cottages that were 'Sold to [the] Infirmary' prior to their demolition in c.1894–95. Their demolition allowed access to the site that had been acquired for the building of the new infirmary. The painting was originally owned by Mr and Mrs H. Agar of 10 North Gate, and donated by their daughter, Mrs J. Nagle, to the League of Friends in memory of her parents in 1987. Courtesy of The League of Friends of Bridgnorth Hospital.

Baker left a 'considerable residue to the two trustees, to be distributed as they should think fit among charities in England, without any restrictions whatever'.[11]

On the morning of Wednesday, 19 December 1894, Messrs Pudsey and Trevor announced at a meeting of the Infirmary Committee that the residue of Mrs Baker's estate would be bequeathed to the Bridgnorth and South Shropshire Infirmary.[12] The 'good fairy' – to quote Mr Bethell – had arrived with a 'Munificent bequest of £7,000', of which £2,000 was allocated to the Building Fund whilst the remainder was retained as an endowment.

Such a bountiful bequest was tempered on the following day by another important issue that required addressing, namely the resignation of the Matron, Miss 'Fanny' Hadfield. After nine-and-a-half years of service, often under difficult circumstances, Miss Hadfield had 'accepted an important post at Bolton' where the former house-surgeon, Dr Horace Jefferies, was in practice! Anxious to commence her duties in the new year, Miss Hadfield had her resignation accepted by the House Committee on 19 December with the following unanimously adopted resolution:

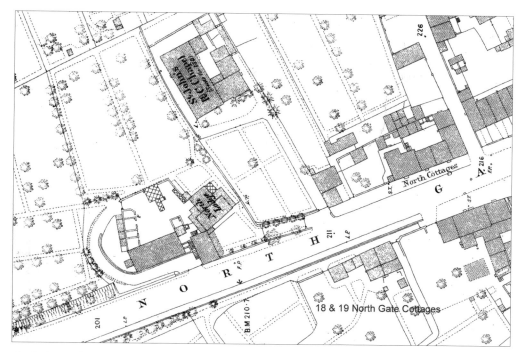

An Ordnance Survey map showing the position of the cottages, 18 and 19 North Gate prior to their demolition in c.1894–95. © Crown Copyright 1884.

> *That the Committee formally ratify the acceptance of Miss Hadfield's resignation by the House Committee and the arrangement by which that resignation should take effect at the end of the year. They are deeply sensible to the very heavy loss which the Infirmary will sustain by the departure of Miss Hadfield. For the past 9½ years, during which time she has held the post of Matron, she has devoted herself with single-minded earnestness to ministering to the needs of the patients and doing all in her power to mitigate their sufferings. As a nurse she has been skilful, attentive and unsparing of herself, as a manager she has been careful, economical and painstaking. The Committee heartily wish her success in her new sphere of labour where they hope she will enjoy long years of useful and happy life, and can assure her that in Bridgnorth and its neighbourhood her departure will be universally regretted, and her name and work will be long remembered.*[13]

This formal accolade was complimented by the raising of a testimonial fund in 'recognition of the value of her services' and as a 'mark of respect' in which Miss Hadfield was 'universally held'. The monies raised enabled the purchase of a silver afternoon tea service and an electroplated hot water jug[14] that, together with a cheque for £30, were presented to Miss Hadfield upon her leaving. The event was briefly reported in the

Bridgnorth Journal on 26 January 1895, the report giving no indication of what was said at the presentation by those present, including Miss Hadfield. The exclusion of her 'voice' from the report is in stark contrast to the reports of departing male house-surgeons, whose presentations were extensively reported – as were their remarks, which appear to have been reproduced verbatim. This biased reporting was not an anomy (an absence of usual social standards) but simply a reflection of the times, as the social and legal status of women, in a predominately patriarchal society, was inferior to that of men, irrespective of an individual woman's standing in the community.

Meanwhile, the Infirmary Committee, aware of Miss Hadfield's impending departure had, by 20 December, appointed a replacement from amongst the 125 candidates who had applied for the 'Matronship' (four of whom were invited to attend for interview). The successful candidate was Miss Hannah Mary Bailie, who was engaged on an annual salary of £50, a sum that would remain unchanged for the next 11 years. Such a paltry remuneration reflects the plethora of 'Trained Hospital Nurses' as demonstrated by the number of nurses applying for the 'Matronship'. Aged about 34 and originally hailing from Lancaster, Miss Bailie was said to have trained at the Guest Hospital, Dudley and afterwards at 'the Sheffield Hospital' where she was registered, in 1891, as a nurse at the Public Hospital and Dispensary. Returning to the Guest Hospital as an 'elected' staff nurse, Miss Bailie was subsequently promoted to the position of 'senior Head Nurse', during which time she 'was always left in charge whenever the Matron was absent'.[15] Said to have been a trained nurse for 'over 5 ½ years' Miss Bailie, who came with 'excellent testimonials and recommendations' would, like Miss Hadfield before her, become an asset to the Infirmary as 'a Matron who did her work in a kind [and] unobtrusive way' whilst maintaining the Infirmary 'in such a state of efficiency' that the Committee could invite visitors to go round the institution 'at any time'.[16]

In the intervening years the house-surgeons had come and gone. The popular Mr House, who had served for three years, departed for Australia (with a testimonial) in the summer of 1891, to be replaced by Mr William Wallace Craig, MRCS (Eng); LRCP (Lon) whose tenure was brief. Resigning in July 1892 to commence a house-surgeon's post at the Salop Infirmary, Mr Craig, a Salopian by birth, would return to Bridgnorth within two years to establish himself as a general medical practitioner. Once in practice other appointments soon followed, including the posts of medical officer to the Bridgnorth Medical Aid Association (1895) and Honorary Surgeon to the Infirmary (a position first recorded in 1896). Those who followed William Craig in 1892 were Stephen Haworth, Arthur Ridsdale, and in 1894 came the appointment of Dr Wilfred Watkins-Pitchford, MB, MRCS, LRCP, who was still in post in early 1895 when progress towards the development of the new infirmary took practical shape.

The revised plans, previously submitted to the Borough Surveyor, now came before the Town Council's General Purpose Committee, where they were considered and approved. With planning approval obtained, Mr Maidman immediately submitted a notice of tender for publication that read:

Bridgnorth and South Shropshire Infirmary
Proposed new building

Builders desirous of tendering for the above works, comprising Administrative Block, Wards for 18 patients, Out-Patients Department and small laundry, etc., are required to send in their names by March 6th, with references to two Architects. Plans and specifications will be on view at Bridgnorth and Bills of Quantities obtained on payment of £1, which will be returned on receipt of a Bona-fide Tender. The Committee do not bind themselves to accept the lowest or any Tender.[17]

By 6 March, 12 builders, from distances far and near, had submitted tenders ranging from £4,368 to £6,064. The successful tender, which was the lowest at £4,368, was that of Mr Ralph Merton Hughes of 255 Bradford Street, Birmingham. On 6 April, he was 'engaged with a larger contract in the West Midlands' where Maidman had visited to appraise his work and testimonials. Satisfied with all that he had seen and heard from the site architect, Mr Maidman reported back to the Infirmary Committee who subsequently awarded Mr Hughes the contract, with penalties attached, to construct the new infirmary. Contractually obliged to complete the building works within ten months of the starting date (that was not recorded), Hughes was also to employ as much local labour as possible[18] to alleviate local levels of unemployment. However, if building works were to commence, following the demolition of the cottages, then a transfer in the ownership of the land was required. This was accomplished through a Deed of Conveyance between Mr William Orme Foster on the one part and the 17 members of the Board of Trustees on the other, each putting their signature to a document on the 25 March 1895.[19] Thereafter, things moved swiftly, as within a matter of weeks Mr Hughes had moved to Bridgnorth and engaged his workforce to prepare the site for the laying of the foundation stone, which took place on the afternoon of Wednesday 24 April 1895.[20]

A civic occasion of 'exceptional public interest and importance', the event commenced with a public luncheon at the Crown Hotel's Assembly Room where a liberal menu, at 2/6 a head, included 13 main courses, many of them seasonal. Amongst the dignitaries present were the High Sheriff of Shropshire, Mr Maidman and his wife, the recently consecrated Bishop of Hereford, Dr Percival (who had accepted the office of Visitor to the Infirmary) and, of course, Mrs W.O. Foster who would lay the foundation stone. Commencing at 2.30 p.m., the proceedings began with a short service. This was followed by the laying of the foundation stone in which a cavity had been made to receive that day's *London Times* and a copy of the *Bridgnorth Journal* for Saturday, 20 April 1895. Then, as was customary, Mrs Foster was presented with a silver trowel and mallet, both of which were dated and inscribed. Presented by Mr T. Martin Southwell on behalf of the Building Committee, the silver trowel was engraved upon its upper surface with the arms of the Foster family and of the Borough of Bridgnorth, whilst the reverse bore the words: 'Presented to Mrs. Foster, of Apley Park, by members of the Building Committee, on the occasion of her laying the foundation stone of the New Infirmary'. Of particular interest is the mallet, for this bore the words: 'This mallet is made of part of a beam from the Friars' Refectory'. As a building, the refectory was once part of the thirteenth-century Franciscan Friary where the Grey Friars had served the community until the Dissolution led to its closure in 1538. Situated on the west bank of the river Severn, the abandoned site was occupied by Messrs Southwell's Carpet Manufactory, whose senior director was Mr T. Martin Southwell.

After further speeches, the ceremony eventually came to a close with a benediction given by the Bishop and the taking of a group photograph to commemorate the event. Guests, including Miss Hadfield, then departed from the scene to the sound of music supplied by the bandsmen of the local Kings Shropshire Light Infantry (KSLI) voluntary battalion. It was an occasion that had involved many in the community, including a Mr Turley who, at the conclusion of the ceremony, 'fired 40 or 50 rounds from anvils in celebration of the event'. Many others in the town and locality had also contributed to the many and various fund-raising activities in support of the Infirmary, which traditionally included annual collections from May Fair Stallage, 'Great Fairs', Hospital Sunday and Hospital Saturday.

As early as 1835, it had been hoped by Coley and others that the local clergy would undertake an occasional charity sermon in aid of the Infirmary. It was a hope denied, particularly by the Revd George Bellett who (according to Coley in his *Faithful Report*, p. 35) 'disapproved of any charity-sermons, except for objects foreign to the town [*sic*]'. Two decades later the local clergy, since *c*.1852, had preached 'Charity Sermons', on an occasional basis, in aid of the Infirmary. However, it was Canon Miller, DD of Birmingham who, in 1858, formalised congregational giving in aid of the Birmingham General Hospital by introducing what became known as Hospital Sunday, a term attributed to the people of Birmingham.[21] Some 15 years later (*c*.1873), this annual act of congregational giving was introduced in Bridgnorth when 24 religious houses, of all denominations within the town and surrounding villages, gave collectively to the Bridgnorth Infirmary.[22] This act of giving was supplemented in 1886 with the introduction of 'Hospital Saturday', the origins of which are unclear. An annual event occurring during the month of September, Hospital Saturday was aimed primarily at the 'working classes' who were paid on a Saturday. This group were also the main beneficiaries of medical attention at the Bridgnorth Infirmary – unlike the 'middle-classes' who were treated privately in their homes and who were perceived by many as contributors to Hospital Sunday.

In 1895 the monies raised from Hospital Sunday and Hospital Saturday were £107 17s 5d and £ 93 13s 3d respectively: figures that had altered little over the decades due, in part, to a relatively static population[23] and cyclical depressions in trade and agriculture with subsequent unemployment. There were other demands of a national nature, such as contributions to the many Imperial War Funds and Queen Victoria's Golden and Diamond jubilee celebrations of 1887 and 1897, all of which placed claims on local giving with a subsequent reduced income for the Infirmary.

At the close of 1895, Dr Watkins-Pitchford had already tendered his resignation having previously introduced a series of separate six-week first aid 'Technical Courses' for the men and women of the St John Ambulance Association. Departing at the end of January 1896, Dr Watkins-Pitchford, like others who had 'endeared' themselves to the community, received a testimonial that took place on Friday 7 February 1896. Described as a man 'who observes nature', the first of the three gifts that he received was an astronomical telescope; the second, a portmanteau and the third, from his 'poorer patients', a set of dessert knives and forks. In giving thanks he reflected upon his 'poorer patients' and in so doing remarked that:

> As a house surgeon to the Infirmary, I have enjoyed an opportunity denied to almost everyone else. I have seen how working people live, I have seen their homes, I have seen them in health, in sickness and alas! in a few cases of death – that time above all others when a man shows his true character. The qualities that have appealed to my admiration above others in our Bridgnorth people are their independence, their good fellowship with one another, their loyalty to the authorities and their employees, but above all, the simplicity of their lives.[24]

This insight into Dr Watkins-Pitchford's patients, the 'working people' of Bridgnorth, partially reveals their moral qualities but fails to inform us of their occupations. From a correspondent to the *Bridgnorth Journal*, whose pseudonym was 'Onlooker', we learn of other 'working people' who sought 'relief' for their minor accidents at the Infirmary, who included, in 'these cycling days', the cyclist. The various occupations described by 'Onlooker' included metalworkers, such as iron founders and blacksmiths who, during the course of their work, sustained 'iron fragments' to their eyes. Other 'working people' were described as bricklayers, hod-men and carpenters, each of whom received treatment for sprained ankles, bruises and cuts.

There were also those who sustained 'various accidents from machinery', whilst the 'agriculturalist' would be treated for being 'ridden over by his horses or falls from [hay] ricks'. Nor were the wives and children of the 'agriculturalists' free from injury, as 'dangerous mishaps by their frequent use of paraffin lamps' suggests that the incidence and treatment of burns was not an uncommon occurrence. According to 'Onlooker', such people 'by their pluck in standing the rigours of a wet and inclement day' at the opening of the new infirmary would reap their rewards someday when 'the fruits of their self-denial [would be] returned to them'.[25] However, 'self-denial' in this context meant giving up a day's work and therefore a day's wages for which there would be no recompense. Nor would the reaping of their rewards come easily, as those members of Bridgnorth's Medical Aid Association and its associated Friendly Societies could attest, for they had struggled long and hard to be represented on the Infirmary Committee.

After five years of striving to achieve their aim, and with the support of two Committee members, the Revd Prebendary Oldham, rector of St Leonard's church, and Dr Rhodes, 'two bona-fide men', were elected to the Infirmary Committee on Tuesday 3 March 1896. Stepping into the shoes of two recently deceased Committee men were Messrs Lancaster and J. Ives who, for the first time in the Infirmary's history, would represent the interests of the working men of Bridgnorth.[26] Perhaps it was no coincidence that in the ensuing years contributions from Hospital Saturday would increase whilst those collections from Hospital Sunday would decrease, especially from the country parishes. This state of affairs was attributed to a seemingly persistent agricultural depression and the 'erroneous belief', both in town and country, that the Infirmary did not need money, which may have been related to the much publicised Baker bequest.

Apart from Messrs Lancaster and Ives, fortune also shone on Mr Hughes, the builder, as good weather had prevailed during the erection of the new infirmary that was nearing completion in March 1896. Completed ahead of schedule, the buildings were open to public view for three consecutive days in July. In due course, the transfer of beds, furniture and patients was made in preparation for the formal opening that took place on Thursday 17 September 1896[27] in 'pelting rain'.

The arrangements for the opening ceremony were extensive and surpassed those that were made for the laying of the foundation stone. Dignitaries, including the Viscountess Boyne who would open the institution, were privately entertained at the Crown Hotel prior to a public luncheon in the adjacent Agricultural Hall. As previously, the staff of the Crown Hotel provided a sumptuous repast, after which the dignitaries departed for the new infirmary to await the arrival of the large procession that had gathered in Low Town at St Mary's School off Severn Street. Led by the band of the local KSLI voluntary battalion, representatives from many organisations participated, including the juvenile and adult branches of Bridgnorth's Friendly Societies. Amongst this group were members of the Bridgnorth Medical Aid Association, whose committee members acted as marshals along the route that the tradesmen and residents of the town had bedecked with bunting. Progressing over the bridge and up the New Road into High Town, the procession eventually arrived at the new infirmary, where the ceremony commenced with a service of dedication led by the Venerable Archdeacon Bather of Ludlow. It then fell to the Chairman of the Building Committee to present Lady Boyne with a gold key (a gift from the architect). Her act of declaring the building open 'was received with much cheering' from the assembled crowd. There now followed a vote of thanks to Lady Boyne by Mr Alfred Trevor in which he acknowledged, before an 'enthusiastic crowd', the contributions made by the town's working poor, remarking that:

> ... The Infirmary had been ably supported by all classes, the rich had given to it out of their abundance but it was pleasant to think that this support had not been limited to the rich alone. (Hear, hear). The heap of small silver coins and copper pennies and half-pennies, amounting to nearly £100, which has been annually cast into the treasury on every hospital Saturday, testified to the loving sympathy and ungrudging liberality of the working men of Bridgnorth who were there that day in their hundreds (Cheers).[28]

Needless to say, there was no mention of working women who, like men, were subject to the vagaries of their employers. In an uncertain world such vulnerability led to the formation of organised labour movements, including Friendly Societies such as the Bridgnorth Medical Aid Association (whose title would become, by 1898, the Bridgnorth Friendly Societies' Medical Association). As Bynum suggests:

> Various fears haunted working-class people in the century: of the workhouse and the hospital, of unemployment and financial incompetence, of old age and a pauper's burial. It was against these uncertainties that workers' association began, especially from the mid-century, to collect weekly payments from members, offering benefits in return if injury, unemployment, sickness, or death disrupted the routine of daily life.[29]

A daily routine that, according to Mr T.M. Southwell, had seen 'working men giving up a day's work to show their sympathy' to the new infirmary in a community where there was 'an absolute union amongst all classes'. Whether such an effusive remark had led some to consider the occasion as a 'red letter day' for Bridgnorth's Friendly Societies is open to question. In an era of social hierarchies, it was the fashionable company – including Dr Jefferies of Bolton – who, at the close of the opening ceremony, would be conducted through the new infirmary buildings to be followed by 'the public' who had waited to view a building that was primarily for their use. Meanwhile, all the town's children, together with those adult members of the friendly societies who had processed, were each presented with a commemorative medal as a gift from the Mayor, Mr Edmund M. Southwell, whose indisposition on the day had been noted with regret.

Visible for all to see to this day is the Infirmary building. Commissioned by the Infirmary Committee in 1893, their design objective was: '... to secure hygienic perfection so compactly planned as to be capable of being worked by a small number of staff ...' in a building that was to have a 'pleasing appearance' and where 'all unnecessary ornamentation' would be avoided.[30] Built in the English domestic style[31] this vernacular building, which was 'suited to its surroundings', was built of Ruabon brick externally and local brick internally, whilst the ornamental portions were hewn from Alveley stone and the roofs covered with 'brindled Broseley tiles'.

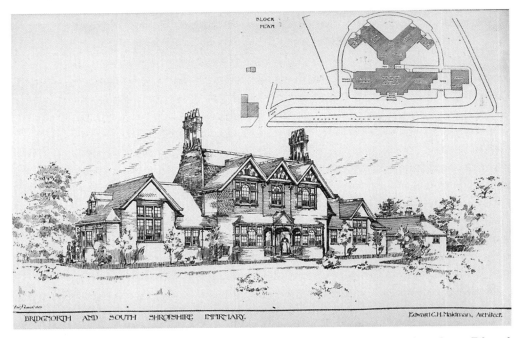

A drawing and block plan of the new Bridgnorth and South Shropshire Infirmary by the architect, Edward C. H. Maidman of Edinburgh, which appeared in The Building News, *February 24, 1899.*
Courtesy of the RIBA Collections.

The groundworks, which were 'arranged on the latest improved sanitary principles', included 'pipes' manufactured by Doulton, each of which had been tested under hydraulic pressure and 'laid on a bed of concrete and so arranged as to be easily inspected and periodically cleansed'. Further design features were the installation of large water tanks in the roof space that would supply hydrants in case of fire, whilst the 'ventilation' had also been 'arranged on the most scientific principles'. This was 'attained by concealed roof ventilators and by fresh-air inlets through hot-water radiators' that, combined with hot-water pipes, were situated throughout the building. Several rooms, including the two wards, were also 'supplemented by fireplaces' for a 'comfortable appearance'.

The concept of 'ventilation' (associated with the hospital design known as the pavilion plan) was reflected in the layout of the building where 'cross ventilation corridors' separated the ground-floor in-patient facilities from the central two-storey block. Within the in-patient area were two 'large' eight-bedded wards whose respective sanitary arrangements were also separated from the wards by further cross-ventilation corridors. Situated behind the central block to the west 'and screened from the east winds', the two wards were designed on the pavilion plan, being rectangular in shape with opposing windows (to allow for cross-ventilation) on an alignment that allowed 'a more even distribution of sunlight than would result from keeping them in a straight line, and also for convenience of administration'.

This design was favoured by Florence Nightingale who, with the Manchester surgeon John Robertson and George Gowin, editor of the architectural journal, *The Builder*, are credited with its introduction in mid-nineteenth-century England.[32] Known as Nightingale wards, each ward would have provided separate accommodation for male and female patients, whilst the children – who were the first patients to be transferred to the new building – would have been placed in the female ward.

Apart from the two 'large' wards that were separated by a 'duty room', there was also a two-bedded private ward that could be converted to a 'special ward' with one bed and one cot, which suggests that it may have been used for a mother and sick child as private maternity cases were excluded from the Infirmary until 1922. There was also an 'operation room', conveniently situated opposite the private ward, for which the resident house-surgeon (Dr William Mott Whitehouse) had donated a 'glass table', whilst one of the Honorary Surgeons, Mr Craig, had given a 'ward dresser wagon' that presumably held all the equipment necessary for the dressing of wounds on ward rounds.

As for the two-storey central block, its ground floor was flanked to the south by the out-patients' department with its separate entrance for the patients, and within, a surgery and a dispensary. On the north was the kitchen that opened out onto a yard and from thence to a much needed modern 'detached laundry and mortuary block'; whilst the wards, as previously mentioned, were located to the west of the central block. The exterior of the two-storey central block, which was 'faced with tile-hanging' on the upper portion of the building was, internally, primarily an administrative area. On the ground floor was the 'principal entrance' that led, via steps to a porch and entrance hall, from which a boardroom and, apparently, a consulting room existed, as did two further rooms, one each being allocated to the house-surgeon and the matron.

Financial constraints meant there was not a separate 'home' for the matron, nurses and servants whose bedrooms (later said to number four) were located on the upper storey; as, presumably, was the house-surgeon's bedroom that conventionally would have been separated from the women's quarters. In the absence of any architectural plans, there is no indication of where various facilities – such as ward sluices, linen

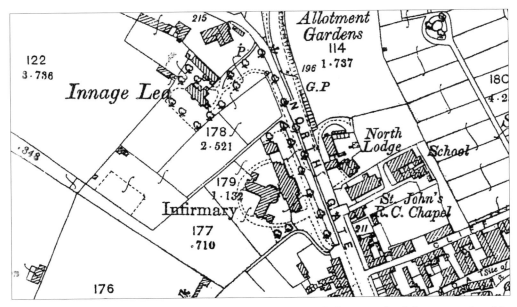

An Ordnance Survey map of North Gate showing the site of the new Infirmary on land that was purchased for £300 and exchanged through a Deed of Conveyance, dated 25 March 1895, between Mr William Orme Foster on the one part and the 17 Trustees of the Infirmary on the other part. © Crown Copyright 1903.

rooms, and staff bathrooms (including lavatories) – were located. Nor is there mention of a chapel at a time when 'next to the Church the hospital might be taken as one of the most fundamental Christian institutions'.[33] However, six members of the local clergy were committed to, and involved with, the management of the Infirmary. Furthermore, as the Infirmary lay within the Parish of St Leonard, the incumbent of St Leonard's Church was invariably appointed as Chaplain to the Infirmary.

Perceived as a 'credit to the town' [and] 'perhaps the first building in the Borough to be built on scientific principles',[34] the new infirmary also required furnishing. This demand fell upon the Honorary Secretary, who established a Furniture Fund and in so doing drew up a list of requirements that was felt by some to be too ambitious. The fear was misplaced as many individuals gave generously, including 'some people in the neighbourhood who thought [that Matron Hadfield's] work should never be forgotten': hence the Hadfield Fund and the purchase of 'certain appliances' (for example trusses and elastic stockings) as a commemorative gift to the new infirmary.[35] The Southwell and Purton families generously met the need for additional beds, whilst Mrs Foster and her daughter furnished the boardroom. The wife of the recently deceased Mr McMichael, previously a member of the Management Committee, donated a consulting room couch, and a Mr Simmonds provided a Bunsen's burner and fittings for the dispensary. Others donated an 'invalid bed' (Mr Perry) and provided furnishings for the wards (Mr Jones, draper, of Waterloo House); whilst Mr Hewett, the Honorary

Treasurer, provided 24 chairs. Other donations included quilts, lockers, ward screens, bed tables, bed rests and clocks for all three wards. There were also donations of various domestic items that included china, crockery and table knives, but no forks or spoons as they, unlike knives, did not come apart with usage. Such gifts were gratefully received and duly acknowledged in a building that eventually cost £6,099 16s 1d to complete. The estimated deficit of £371 19s 5d, which was gradually reduced through further appeals, was eventually signed off in 1900, much to the relief of those concerned.

Having furnished the Infirmary, there was one further and final administrative act that required attention: a revision of the Rules and Regulations. This task was accomplished on 17 September 1897 when the Trustees passed nine Fundamental Rules and fifty-four Bye-Laws (or regulations) that addressed the governance of the Infirmary.[36] Included amongst the Bye-Laws were the duties and obligations of the Honorary-Surgeons who numbered three (a figure that became contentious with the introduction of the National Insurance Act of 1911) and who were required to be 'duly qualified Practitioners residing within one mile of the Town Hall' (Bye-Law No. 9). Conversely, the resident house-surgeon had to 'be a legally qualified practitioner' (Bye-Law No. 14). Obliged to abide by 13 Bye-Laws and remain in post for one year, the house-surgeon was also required to give two months' notice or forfeit his salary should he leave before his term of office was completed. By comparison, the Matron had to abide by four Bye-Laws, which are given in full:

Matron

27. That the Matron receive such Annual Salary as the Committee shall from time to time appoint, that she reside in the Institution, manage the housekeeping and have control over the Nurses and Servants under the general direction of the Committee and Honorary Surgeons, and that she provide diets for the In-Patients under the directions of the Surgeons and the House Surgeon.

28. That she render an account of all housekeeping expenses to the House Committee at their monthly meetings.

29. That she be allowed a holiday of three weeks during the year at such times as may be appointed by the House and Surgical Committees, and that she arrange that every nurse employed in the Institution be allowed a holiday of the same length.

30. That she give two months' notice to the Committee, or forfeit two months' salary before she quits the service of the Infirmary; and that she may be summarily dismissed by the Committee at any time for misconduct or neglect of duty without being entitled to receive any salary except for services actually performed during her residence in the Infirmary.[37]

Such regulations suggest that the Matron's role was largely administrative, but in this small general hospital she was also obliged to undertake other tasks including: nursing the sick, undertaking the work of the house-surgeon in his absence (including dispensing and, with the other nurses, visiting out-patients in their homes). The practice of visiting out-patients in their homes had reduced in scope and would virtually cease in 1898 when, in the following year, other demands would be placed upon Matron Bailie and her nurses (the names of whom went unreported, as did the numbers employed at the Infirmary).

Table 5. Financial statements: Probationers, Outside Nursing & Infirmary 1899–1913

Year	Probationers' Fees Income	Probationers' Uniform Expenditure	Outside Nursing Income	Infirmary Total receipts
	£ s d	£ s d	£ s d	£ s d
1899	£10. 0s. 0d	£2. 13s. 8d	Scheme starts	£823. 10s. 11d
1900	£33. 8s. 0d	£6. 1s. 2d	'A few cases'	£794. 9s. 5d
1901	£15. 0s. 0d	£6. 4s. 0d	£12. 12s. 0d	£811. 0s. 9d
1902	None listed	£4. 15s. 5d	£22. 18s. 0d	£850. 0s. 1d
1903	£10. 0s. 0d	£7. 4s. 10d	£49. 16s. 4d	£876. 0s. 6d
1904	£10. 0s. 0d	£8. 2s. 6d	£66. 1s. 0d	£900. 10s. 0d
1905	£10. 0s. 0d	£1. 19s. 11d	£56. 4s. 3d	£916. 19s. 11d
1906	£15. 0s. 0d	£6. 17s. 9d	£67. 4s. 0d	£934. 16s. 6d
1907	£15. 0s. 0d	£5. 15s. 11d	£68. 13s. 1d	£918. 17s. 2d
1908	£10. 0s. 0d	£3. 8s. 3d	£71. 8s. 5d	£909. 17s. 9d
1909	£15. 0s. 0d	£6. 8s. 11d	£95. 5s. 0d	£916. 14s. 8d
1910	£1. 1s. 0d	£1. 11s. 9d	£116. 7s. 0d	£930. 16s. 7d
1911	£1. 1s. 0d	£2. 17s. 11d	£63. 12s. 6d	£970. 2s. 0d
1912	£5. 0s. 0d	£6. 10s. 3d	£41. 18s. 6d	£943. 0s. 2d
1913	£5. 0s. 0d	None listed	£32. 12s. 0d	£873. 6s. 3d
Totals	£155. 10s. 0d	£70. 12s. 3d	£764. 12s. 1d	£13370. 2s. 8d

Source: Bridgnorth Hospital Records: Treasurer's Revenue Accounts, Receipts and Expenditures for years 1889 to 1913

A new development at this time was the introduction of 'Probationers' and 'Outside Nursing', both of which were introduced in 1899, mainly to enhance the Infirmary's finances. Probationers, who could loosely be described as student nurses, paid an (unreported) individual fee for the privilege of becoming an apprenticed nurse. The probationers were provided with a uniform and trained by Matron Bailie, but the scheme apparently ceased in 1914 with the advent of the First World War, and would not resume until 1921 when a new Matron was appointed to the Infirmary. From a financial perspective, little appears to have been gained by the initiative as the total income from probationers' fees over the 15-year period (1899–1913 inclusive) was reported as £155 10s, whilst the total expenditure on uniforms amounted to £70 12s 3d. The presence of the probationers did, however, allow the trained nurses to undertake 'Outside Nursing' that entailed administering to sick fee-paying patients in their private households.

Referred to as the 'Private Nurses' Department', its uptake by private patients was initially slow and reflected in the receipts, wherein payments – if there were any – were not separated from 'Payments on behalf of various patients'. However, in 1901 'considerable use [had] been made of the services of the nurses of the Institution to nurse private cases outside the Infirmary',[38] which brought in £12 12s and warranted the introduction of 'Regulations for Private Nurses'[39]. Financially, 'Outside Nursing' proved more lucrative, as the total income over the same 15-year period realised a sum of £764 12s 1d (although this cannot be reliably confirmed); however, the combined incomes from both these schemes (assuming that the Infirmary reports are reliable) represented 6.9 per cent of the Infirmary's total income of £13,370 2s 8d over the same 15-year period (Table 5).

As a scheme, 'Outside Nursing' did bring much wanted additional monies to the Infirmary but increasingly fee-paying patients chose to enter the institution as inpatients, where they too were obliged to comply with regulations for 'Paying Patients'.

By December 1899, changes amongst the medical staff were also occurring, due in part to the failing health of the Consulting Surgeon Mr Mathias, who would die on 5 January 1900, aged 71. He was first recorded as an Honorary-Surgeon in 1852, but at the 'Stormy Meeting' of 1891, when the state of the old Infirmary came under scrutiny (including the allegation that the 'bedsteads were found to be swarming with vermin') Mr Mathias was unfazed as he declared that:

> When he was at King's College Hospital, London, he had dressed patients there and had seen flees hop out and bugs there too. The place used there was an old workhouse at the back of Lincolns Inn. Their [Bridgnorth] Infirmary was a palace to what that was.[40]

At Christmas the house-surgeon Mr John Cayley Padwick, MRCS (Eng), LRCP (Lon), resigned his post, as did the Honorary-Surgeon, Mr Alfred Bethell. Neither, however, would sever their connections with the Infirmary, as Mr Bethell became a Consulting Surgeon to the institution whilst Mr Padwick entered into a partnership with Mr Bethell and was duly appointed as an Honorary-Surgeon to the Infirmary; a seemingly convenient arrangement. Mr Bethell's name remained on the Infirmary's

Report Book until 1911, and thereafter there is no mention of him; unlike Mr Padwick, who retained his position until 1918 having served his country with the Royal Army Medical corps (RAMC) during the First World War.

One name, however, that consistently appears in the records is that of Mr William Orme Foster (1814–99) who, in 1867, purchased the Apley Park estate from the Whitmore family for the remarkable sum of £565,000; a value that today (2017) equates to approximately 58 million pounds.[41] It was an acquisition that brought with it an opportunity, or indeed an obligation, to dispense patronage, including support of the Bridgnorth Infirmary where he became a trustee and a benefactor (but not its President as that was the prerogative of the Whitmore family). Described as one of the Midlands' 'great ironmasters', Foster married Isabella Grazebrook of Liverpool in 1843, who bore him two sons and four daughters.[42] His heir, William Henry Foster would, upon his father's death on 29 September 1899, take on the mantle of Trustee to the Infirmary. In 1907, William became its President following the death of Thomas Charles Douglas Whitmore, who had represented the Apley interest for nearly 40 years. As for the role of President, it was one that Mr W.H. Foster would come to question in the decades ahead when confronted with the difficulties that originated with the introduction of the 1911 National Insurance Act.

As for the old Infirmary on Holly Bush Road, that too had undergone change, for on 23 December 1896 the property reverted to Mr Thomas Charles Douglas Whitmore, a grandson of Thomas Whitmore of Apley Park, whose patronage had enabled the old Infirmary to be erected on Apley land. With the estate long gone, Thomas C.D. Whitmore placed the old infirmary and its grounds up for sale, which took place at the Crown Hotel on Thursday 25 February 1897. Erected at a cost of £840, the property was purchased for the sum of £400 by a Wellington solicitor on behalf of others.[43] These others finally emerged on 26 May 1897 when the Roman Catholic Bishop-elect of Shrewsbury, the Revd D. Allen, officially opened a religious house. Those that entered the house were 'a small contingent of Sisters of Mercy from the Mother House in Shrewsbury',[44] whose presence provided a fitting end for the old Infirmary where the cure and care of the body, combined with the saving of souls, had been a priority for all those who had served its purpose.

A small but important facility, the old Infirmary, with all its imperfections, had served a pressing need for those who lived and worked in a predominately rural community. The new and comparatively large Infirmary, decidedly fit for the age, would continue to serve the community in a new century in which yet more change and an uncertain future lay ahead.

7 DEFIANT DOCTORS

In the House of Commons, on Wednesday, Mr Hunt (U[nionist], – Ludlow Division) asked the Chancellor of the Exchequer [Mr David Lloyd George] why the panel in the Bridgnorth area of Shropshire was closed from January 15th, and was still to be closed for a period of three years. Mr. Masterman, who replied, said as the number of [medical] practitioners available for the panel system in the urban and rural areas of Bridgnorth was not adequate for treatment of insured persons, the Commissioners dispensed with the necessity for the adoption of the panel system for the period named, and authorised the Insurance Committee to make other arrangements under Section 15 of the Act.

The *Bridgnorth Journal*, Saturday 15 February 1913

T HE question raised in Parliament by Mr Rowland Hunt, MP related to the National Insurance Act of 1911 and specifically to the introduction of Part 1, the health insurance scheme. At Bridgnorth, three general medical practitioners – all of whom were Honorary Surgeons at the Infirmary – had refused to work the Act. Their intransigence therefore denied the many insured working-poor access to health care under the insurance scheme. To rectify this situation 'other arrangements' were made by the Shropshire Insurance Committee who, under Section 15 of the Act, appointed two 'duly qualified medical practitioners'[1] thus enabling the Act to come into force at Bridgnorth in January 1913.

This resolution of one problem led inexorably to other 'insuperable problems' at the Infirmary where, in the opening decade of a new century, the inevitable process of change continued. Following the death of Alfred Mathias another death occurred during the year of 1900: that of the Honorary Oculist, Dr William Charnley, who had attended the Shrewsbury Eye, Ear and Throat Hospital since 1887.[2] The date of Dr Charnley's appointment to the Infirmary is unknown but his position reflected a wider development that had occurred from the mid-nineteenth century onwards: that of the hospital specialist. His successor, both at Shrewsbury and Bridgnorth, was Dr C.G. Russ Wood who now bore the title of Consulting Ophthalmic Surgeon. This, in turn, reflected the development of the speciality within medicine.

This same year also saw a Miss E.E. Powell offering her services as an Honorary District Nurse to the Infirmary,[3] where nurses only undertook a 'certain amount' of domiciliary visits to the sick poor. Under the direction of the medical staff, Miss Powell's activities went unreported, as did her departure; but on the 6 December 1900 came the appointment of a new house-surgeon, Dr Louis Edington Dickson, MB, MRCS, LRCS. Resigning in 1904 to work elsewhere, Dr Dickson returned to Bridgnorth in 1907, where he established himself as a GP, entered into a partnership with Dr Padwick, married Dr William Rhodes' daughter, and became an Honorary Surgeon to the Infirmary alongside his two senior colleagues, Doctors Craig and Padwick.

This trio of medical men will be met with again, but in 1901 the appointment of another specialist occurred: that of the Honorary Dental Surgeon, Mr L.H. Beaumont, LDS, whose tenure ceased around 1910. Thereafter the post remained vacant until 1916 when Mr Alexander Grant Legge, LDS was appointed as his successor. Their respective appointments did not preclude the doctors, including a dextrous house-surgeon, from practicing dentistry, which in previous and future years appears to have consisted of tooth extractions for a nominal sum. In earlier years, anyone with an aptitude for dentistry could extract teeth; however, the introduction of the Dentists' Act of 1878 required those who practiced dentistry (except doctors) to enrol on the Dentists' Register having previously gained the Licentiate of Dental Surgery (LDS) from the Royal College of Surgeons of either England, Edinburgh, Glasgow or Ireland.[4] A similar demand had been placed upon medical men with the introduction of the Medical Act of 1858. Both Acts sought to regularise the respective professions of medicine and dentistry, with the intention to exclude 'quacks' – unqualified and unorthodox practitioners – and to protect the public (and, it has to be said, the professions) from irregular practitioners.

Meanwhile the Infirmary Committee had frequently found it difficult to obtain 'Letters' for certain patients requiring a period of convalescence. This difficulty evaporated in 1905 when the Trustees of the Lady Forester Convalescent Home at Llandudno – a fashionable Welsh seaside resort – 'kindly extended the benefits of that excellent Institution to the patients of the Bridgnorth Infirmary ... free of all charge'.[5] The benefactress was the late Mary Anne, the Lady Forester who, in 1862, had married the Honourable George Cecil Weld Forester of Willey Park, Broseley. Upon her death in 1893 the Lady Forester left a considerable legacy that was to be used in the building of a cottage hospital and a convalescent home as memorials to her late husband who had died in 1886.[6]

The legacy, which the *Bridgnorth Journal* reported in January 1898 as being £440,000, would ultimately establish cottage hospitals in Much Wenlock and Broseley, the Shropshire Convalescent and Surgical Home at Baschurch and the Llandudno Convalescent Home. The latter was an impressive 50-bed home set within an 18-acre landscaped site, which opened on 17 October 1904. The appointment of a Matron had occurred in the previous year, and of the 133 applicants 'Number 5' was none other than Matron Bailie of the Bridgnorth Infirmary, whose testimonials were returned to her on 22 September 1903; the post of Matron being awarded to Miss K. Elphick of the Herefordshire General Hospital in Hereford.[7]

Those convalescent patients who attended the Home were categorised into three classes, each class being permitted a stay of two weeks – or more for those who could afford to extend their residency. Class Three represented private patients who incurred a charge of 35s, whilst Class Two consisted of those who could afford a small sum of money (perhaps 20s). Alternatively, Class One represented certain occupations whose stay of two weeks (including rail travel) was entirely free when spent in general rooms and dormitories. This was the category extended to the patients of the Bridgnorth Infirmary where those defined under Class One were: 'Labourers, Artisans, Clerks, Small shopkeepers, Small farmers, Domestic Servants not in service with any of the above and persons in a similar position'.[8]

Described as 'well equipped and excellently managed', the Lady Forester Llandudno Convalescent Home was one of many that were established by this time. Similarly, nursing homes were also proving popular, being places where, according to the newly appointed Infirmary President, Mr William Henry Foster, the 'public appreciated the value of good nursing'. This remark, made in 1907, was a response to a suggestion that a general nursing home might be 'set up' at some time in the future. Not only would it benefit the community – for those who could afford it – but also provide a source of income for the Infirmary. In response, the Revd Lester suggested that if not a nursing home then perhaps a 'trained nurse who might go about amongst the poor without payment' as this 'would be of the greatest possible blessing to the town':[9] a remark that suggests Miss Powell had vacated her post and that, indirectly, her work amongst the poor had been recognised.

Neither a nursing home nor an honorary district nurse materialised, for in the interim the Honorary Secretary, the Revd John Wright, was formulating other ideas. He recognised, as did others, that Outside Nursing was providing a 'source of profit' for the Infirmary. However, an insufficient number of nurses resulted in the demands of the Infirmary taking priority over those households that required a private nurse. What the Infirmary needed was more nurses who 'could do more remunerative outside nursing'. Required to live in, the nurses and servants were 'already inconveniently crowded' in the existing residential accommodation, which therefore required enlarging. Writing in a private capacity to Mr Maidman, the architect of the Infirmary, the Revd Wright sought advice on the possibility of providing additional accommodation for the staff. He also emphasised that any future scheme would be dependent on 'unexpected' funds becoming available. In reply, Mr Maidman provided a sketch plan of an additional building, the cost of which was estimated at £550.[10]

In late August 1908, news came of an unexpected legacy of £841 from the estate of the late Mrs Yearsley. Assured of funds, the idea was to become a reality, but then an equally unexpected event occurred: the tragic death of Dr William Rhodes at his residence, North Gate House, on 10 September 1908. Two days later the *Bridgnorth Journal* confirmed any rumours that might have circulated in the town when a graphic account of his death and subsequent inquest was published. Aged 56 years, Dr Rhodes had diligently served the Infirmary since 1882 as an honorary surgeon and subsequently as a trustee. He had, like James Milman Coley before him, also served the community as Mayor and afterwards as a magistrate of the Borough. Dr Rhodes was also perceived as being 'greatly liked professionally', with a 'care and kindly consideration for his patients', and his funeral, held at St Leonard's Church, was attended by 'very many of the deceased gentleman's poorer patients' (who, with others, had ignored the family's request for a private service).

Twenty days later another dedicated supporter and trustee of the Infirmary died in his 86th year: Mr Thomas Martin Southwell who, with Dr Rhodes, had championed the building of the new Infirmary. Reduced to seven trustees – the lowest number now permitted by the revised Trust Deed (1897) – other trustees were appointed, including the businessman, Mr A.J. Buston of Astbury Hall and Dr Craig of St John's Priory; both of whom would, in their respective ways, influence future proceedings at the Infirmary. There was also the question of who should succeed Dr Rhodes as honorary surgeon to the Infirmary. The position was subsequently assigned to Dr Dickson who now joined his senior colleagues, Doctors Craig and Padwick, both of whom were influential members of the Management and House Committees. These two medical men were also medical officers (MOs) to the Bridgnorth Friendly Societies Medical Association, where a vacancy existed for a third MO following the death of Dr Rhodes – one that would be filled by Dr Dickson when he was duly elected to the post at the Association's annual meeting in March 1909. In the following month of April, and with a portion of the Yearsley legacy remaining after the building of the nurses' accommodation, other building works were approved and subsequently commenced. A small extension contained a 'much needed additional ward for private cases', complete with adjoining sanitary arrangements. This, Dr Craig had welcomed, for in his opinion it had been 'wanted for a long time', and as a consequence it would be a 'great boon to [the] people of the district'. Other works included the provision of a small surgery and improvements to the operating room. Illuminated by gas lighting until 1919 when electric light was installed (thanks to the Crown and Raven Hotel who had spare capacity from their own generated supply), the operating room was also updated with a 'properly tiled' floor and a proper operating table; an acquisition 'which they had required all along'. An additional nurse – rather than nurses – would also be employed which, it was suggested, would negate the need to employ extra nurses from Wolverhampton. Finally, any monies that remained would be spent on surgical instruments as and when required.[11]

These alterations and additions, undertaken primarily to improve the surgical facilities and provide additional private patient capacity, were perceived as providing a better financial return compared with that from investing in Outside Nursing. From Dr Craig's remarks there is also a suggestion that private patients – often encouraged by doctors – were willing to enter the Infirmary, for there was by this time an appreciation by affluent individuals that it was safer to undergo a procedure in a hospital than a domestic home. This appreciation, or convenience, apparently grew, as in 1924 it was suggested that the support of the Infirmary should be 'general' and not 'private' (a remark that suggests the use of 'pay-beds' was a questionable development, especially at a time when socialism was challenging the status quo). However, by 1910 the Infirmary's finances had become 'exceedingly serious', which had prompted Matron Bailie in the previous year to suggest the introduction of a 'Pound Day'. At this annual event, held in July, the supporters of the Infirmary were encouraged to provide foodstuffs, by the pound weight, to assist in the reduction of the housekeeping expenses.

Aside from the financial uncertainties there were also other anxieties amongst the population at large: the fear of invasion. Tensions existed at home, in Britain's colonies where the regular army was engaged in North Africa, and in Europe where Germany, now a united state, was occupied in military expansionism. To safeguard the Home Front, the Government in the person of R.B. Haldane, Secretary of State for War, introduced various initiatives including the Voluntary Aid Detachment (VAD) scheme in 1909. The aim of the scheme was to supplement 'the imperfect medical services' provided by the Territorial Forces with trained volunteers who would provide 'medical assistance' at a local level. The formal response in Bridgnorth to this War Office scheme occurred at a public meeting on 1 February 1911, when Mr and Mrs W.H. Foster of Apley Park were duly elected as President and Lady President respectively.[12] Ultimately, three Voluntary Aid Detachments were formed: one of men (Bridgnorth, No. 13), who were trained in first aid, and two of women (Bridgnorth, No. 28 and Worfield, No. 42) who were trained in first aid and home-nursing. Those in Bridgnorth were trained by Dr Dickson as MO to the Bridgnorth Detachments, and all subsequently examined by doctors from outside the town. The three detachments also met annually for a joint training exercise when they were assessed, following a battle scenario, on the extraction of the wounded. The exercise was inspected by an officer of the Royal Army Medical Corps (RAMC) who, in 1914, was 'very well pleased with what he had seen'. He also reminded the volunteers that:

> it was necessary to know a great deal more than first-aid and home-nursing in order
> to fulfil all the duties that would devolve upon them in removing and caring for the
> wounded between the field ambulance in the front and the general hospital in the rear.[13]

This responsibility would not be realised by the VAD members until 1915; but in 1911 there was another national issue that was creating uncertainty: the introduction of the National Insurance Act and its associated health insurance scheme. Introduced by the Liberal politician, David Lloyd George (1863–1945), the scheme was known as the 'panel system'. Based on the insurance principle, the scheme ensured that contributing wage-earners from 16–70 years of age with an annual income of under £160[14] were entitled to health care – as a 'panel patient' – from those 'panel doctors' who had agreed to work the Act. Promulgated by Lloyd George as getting 'ninepenny-worth for fourpence', the scheme involved contributions from wage-earners (4d), the employer (3d), and the state (2d); as Davis explains:

> Employers would deduct their employees' contributions from wages and add their
> own, conveying the total to government by purchasing stamps from the post office
> to be fixed to each contributor's card. The government would remit this money,
> augmented by the state contribution, to the 'approved societies' charged with
> operating the Act.[15]

One of the 'approved societies' in Bridgnorth was the Friendly Societies' Medical Association, whose concerns at the introduction of the Act were many, including competition from the big insurance companies such as the Prudential and the Pearl. Their primary concern, however, was the potential loss of their male membership, which became a reality in January 1913 with the implementation of the Act. This reality was cushioned by the introduction of a female approved section (No. 2096) that provided health care to dependants, including children, all of whom were excluded from the 1911 Act.

The Act also had ramifications for the voluntary hospital sector, including the Bridgnorth Infirmary, where an immediate concern in April 1911 was an accumulated debit balance that had required the use of capital to defray expenses. Frustrated by the continuing lack of support from the community, the President wrote a letter – the first of several – to the *Bridgnorth Journal*, in which he commented that 'the Committee should not be in the position of carrying on a hand-to-mouth policy, but should have ample funds available to meet an occasional deficit'.[16] He therefore appealed to the townspeople and 'All Employers of Labour in the District' to help the Infirmary by becoming annual subscribers. The plea went unheeded as the income of £330 9s 6d from annual subscribers in 1911 fell to £317 17s 6d in the following year; a sum that would be reduced in the ensuing years due, in part, to the 'insuperable problems' that arose at the Infirmary and world events that resonated in Bridgnorth where fortunes would change.

Adding to this financial anxiety was the introduction of the National Insurance Act and the effect it might have upon the Infirmary as a voluntary hospital. As a consequence, representatives of the Infirmary were dispatched to London to attend a meeting of the British Hospitals' Association, which, according to the Infirmary's annual report, took place on Friday, 3 June 1911 at the Westminster Palace Hotel. In *The Times* newspaper of 3 June 1911 there is a report of a British Hospitals' Association meeting that took place on the previous day and in a different location. Attended by 'about 200' institutions from across the country, perhaps it was this meeting that included the representatives of the Bridgnorth Infirmary? Irrespective of this discrepancy the meeting, held at St George's Hospital and chaired by its treasurer, predicted an uncertain future for voluntary hospitals. A primary concern was the cost of insurance contributions for nurses and other hospital employees who, whilst in the service of a voluntary hospital:

> ought to be exempted from the provisions of the Bill, for so long as they were resident in the hospital they would presumably be treated inside the hospital and they would, therefore, never qualify for the State benefits.[17]

The assumption was misplaced as the Infirmary's expenditure on 'Insurance for Staff' rose from 2gns in 1911 to '£4 18s 4d (including National Health Insurance)' in 1912;[18] an expenditure that would increase in subsequent years. Speculation on financial matters was rife, as it was thought that voluntary hospitals would lose, either in whole or in part, legacies, donations, subscriptions and contributions towards the Hospital Saturday Fund from the working class. It was also thought that the work of the out-patient departments might lessen, whilst the work of the in-patient departments, 'the most important part of their work', (a phrase subsequently repeated at Infirmary meetings) would increase. There was also the suggestion that State aid should be made available to voluntary hospitals; a notion that was politely dismissed, as any State subsidy implied State intervention in the form of inspections and the auditing of accounts (something not objected to in principle as voluntary hospitals had 'nothing to conceal'). For others, however, State aid meant the demise of the voluntary hospital movement, for there would be little incentive to 'collect from the charitable public'[19]; a sentiment that would be shared by others at the Bridgnorth Infirmary.

For any prospective hospital patient, powerless to intervene, there was also uncertainty as the National Insurance Act excluded hospital provision, including for those who were acutely ill or seriously injured. Ophthalmic and dental services, meanwhile, although dependent upon discretionary benefits, could be obtained through some approved societies.[20] Prior to 1913, all these services were available at the Infirmary and open to all, including the working poor; but in 1913 difficulties arose that would affect all those associated with the panel system and, by extension, those at the Infirmary who were sympathetic to their cause.

A fourth and powerful grouping, who would be affected by the introduction of the health insurance scheme, was the medical profession, and particularly GPs whose representative body, the British Medical Association (BMA), started a 'militant movement against the Insurance Act'[21] in 1911. Fearful that they would lose their independence only to 'become cogs in a bureaucratic machine run by the State!',[22] no fewer than 26,000 doctors out of an estimated 29,000 had, by 1912, signed up to a policy of 'no panel' having pledged 'to take no service under the Act unless and until conditions satisfactory to the association have been conceded'.[23] Lloyd George did make some concessions, including the demand that doctors be represented on Insurance Committees whose remit was to organise a 'panel' from which doctors were selected. A further concession was an improved capitation fee, a fixed payment for each 'panel' patient, separate from treatment costs that, by 31 December 1912, had motivated a sufficient number of doctors to sign the official document of acceptance and thus form the new medical service. Assured of a reliable income from the State, most doctors chose pragmatism. Others, however, remained unyielding, including those who attended a meeting of the Shropshire and Mid-Wales branch of the BMA on 10 December 1912, where it was resolved:

> That in the opinion of the Shropshire and Mid-Wales Branch of the British Medical Association, the result of the conference with the Chancellor of the Exchequer is most unsatisfactory, and the conditions remain unworkable and derogatory to the profession and fatal to an efficient medical service; therefore it urges all practitioners to refuse to enter into agreements with the Local Insurance Committees on those lines.[24]

Attending the BMA branch meeting, held at the Salop Infirmary, were 95 doctors of whom 82 were BMA members and 13 non-members. None have been identified due to a lack of surviving records, except a Dr Gardner who was reported as chairing the meeting. From the provincial section of the 1913 *Medical Directory*[25] – to which doctors supplied information for insertion – it is known that Doctors Craig and Padwick were members of the BMA whereas Dr Dickson gave no mention of his membership, if any, and was not obliged to do so. Unlike their forbear, Dr James Milman Coley, whose reported views on the Poor Law Amendment Act (1834) were publicly stated, Doctors Craig, Padwick and Dickson remain silent on their objections to the National Insurance Act of 1911. Discretion also existed at the offices of the *Bridgnorth Journal,* for at no time were the names of the dissenting doctors published other than to report that there were 'difficulties at Bridgnorth, where the doctors refuse to go on the panel'. This situation, however, was resolved on Tuesday 14 January 1913 when the Shropshire Insurance Committee appointed two young men by the names of Dr Noel Edmund Berry and Dr Alfred Evan Lewis Devonald, both of St George's Hospital, London, as full-time doctors to Bridgnorth.[26] Of the two, Dr Berry was the senior by qualification (1910) and by appointment, as his selection had occurred two hours before that of Dr Devonald, who had qualified in 1911. Initially accommodated at No. 56, High Street, they immediately commenced their joint 'panel' practice. One month later, a notice in the *Bridgnorth Journal* informed the reading public that:

> *Those of the local doctors in the Bridgnorth Union* [workhouse] *and urban district who joined in the Government panel, and also the two medical gentlemen from London, are not confined to the working of the Act, but may also take on private practice.*[27]

By late March Dr Berry, who would marry in the following month, was on duty whilst Dr Devonald took time off to attend the annual dinner (held at the Falcon Hotel in Low Town) of the Dudley-based Midland Counties Mutual Benefit Society. During the dinner the Society's solicitor, Mr W.H. Thompson, proposed a toast to the 'President and Officers of the Bridgnorth district, and the medical profession' in which he referred to the 'somewhat extraordinary state of things in this town' of Bridgnorth where 'the doctors practically boycotted the panel, and would not go upon it'. Although 'not a great lover of the Insurance Act' he believed that when it came into force it was 'the duty of everybody to try to make it a success', including doctors, who had been 'met in a liberal spirit in the terms they had got'. Rising to acknowledge the toast, Dr Devonald diplomatically informed the gathering that he came as a private individual and therefore would not be commenting on Mr Thompson's remarks that had been expressed 'in a very delicate way'. Knowing of Dr Berry's pending marriage and now aware that the Society had several thousand pounds to invest, Dr Devonald audaciously asked if the Society might invest some of it in a house 'for he wanted one': preferably on a 21 years' lease 'if they liked'. Continuing, he referred to those working men who had attended his medical practice over the past months. Given below, the remarks offer an insight of how the sick working men of Bridgnorth responded to the introduction of the health insurance scheme:

The doctor was sometimes described as a necessary evil. No doubt he was; and in connection with large friendly societies he had, of course, to consider the patients, and at the same time he must consider the society. The term, "Going on the Box" was new to him, and he had only been concerned with the sickness side of the question, but when he saw men protesting against going on, and could only be induced to do so when the wife was called in, there was not any fear of malingering. Whilst on his legs he would like to say that he thought they deserved the highest compliment – he was speaking of the whole of the friendly societies in Bridgnorth – and he could say without flattery in any shape or form, that of the 1,200 or more members of friendly societies in the town he could put his finger on one only who had tried to do him. He did not, of course, know how many had done him. (Laughter). He thought that spoke well for the honesty and integrity of the men of Bridgnorth. They seemed to try and give the doctor as little trouble as possible. Scores of men had come to his surgery who ought to have been in bed, and he had the greatest difficulty in sending them back and getting them to bed. He thanked them for coupling his name with the toast, and for the way they had received it; and he assured them that whatever happened he would always feel that he was lucky in having come to Bridgnorth (Applause).[28]

On 28 October 1913 Doctors Berry and Devonald (the latter now ensconced at 'Fern Cliff', Oldbury Wells) applied to the Bridgnorth Friendly Societies' Medical Association to be added to their list of medical officers. The outcome was revealed, including, for the first time, the names of Bridgnorth's dissenting doctors on 7 April 1914 when the Association's President stated that following Berry and Devonald's application:

The matter was discussed, and after full consideration it was decided that in the interest of the members it was advisable to accept their offer. The Association, in the past, had exercised the privilege of engaging all the medical gentlemen in the town, and as the panel doctors now had charge of upwards of 75 per cent of the industrial classes in their district, it was thought that their appointment would be carrying out the principle, and possibly avoid friction in having two doctors attending different members in the same family. It was a matter of regret that as soon as this action on the part of the Committee became known, Messrs. Craig, Padwick, and Dickson sent in their resignations and ceased their connection with the Association from the 1st April … But the gentlemen referred to had not only severed their connection with the Association, they had also organised a combination on similar lines, in direct competition with them.[29]

United in a common purpose, Doctors Craig, Padwick and Dickson established a 'Medical Aid' club into which contributors made quarterly payments on Saturdays;

a scheme that was born out of friction and one that the Association had tried to 'smooth over' when difficulties arose owing to the presence of the panel doctors. These were difficulties that Doctors Berry and Devonald regretted and hoped would be overcome with the assistance of the Association's committee.

There were also difficulties at the Infirmary. Commencing in 1913 following the introduction of the National Insurance Act in July 1912, there was a perception amongst insured working people that the Infirmary would not admit them for treatment. It was a perception, or complaint, that had reached Dr Craig's ears for:

> *He had heard that it had been stated that they would not take insured patients, and*
> *he was glad to have the opportunity of stating in public that they had always been*
> *prepared to take Insurance Act patients the same as others.*[30]

However, this preparedness came with conditions. The subscribers – 'who were not obliged to give a ticket to anyone' – now had the onerous responsibility of ascertaining how much an insured individual would contribute towards their upkeep whilst under treatment in the Infirmary. Considered to be a condition for admission, contributions of 5s or 2s 6d were suggested, although discretion could be exercised according to an individual's means.[31] Upon admission, the insured patient then 'had to come before the resident surgeon, who enquired into the case, and if a proper case for admission it was treated there, and if not a proper case was sent back to the Insurance doctors'.[32] Those insured patients who were 'a proper case for admission' were, however, denied the professional services of their panel doctors whilst in the Infirmary. This situation was one that the Friendly Societies Medical Association had attempted to resolve through approaches to the Infirmary's Management Committee (upon which the three Honorary Surgeons sat) but without success. There was, however, a concession: Doctors Berry and Devonald could come as 'visitors on ordinary visiting days', but definitely not in their professional capacity; a directive that engendered 'very sore feelings amongst the working class'[33] who, increasingly, were unwilling to subscribe to the Infirmary.

For Doctors Berry and Devonald, knowing that 'the present medical staff were hostile to them and boycotted them in every way',[34] their only option was to treat their patients in their own homes (they had yet to establish a separate surgery at No. 12, Whitburn Street), or to refer them to hospitals in Wolverhampton, Kidderminster or London. This action was detrimental to the Infirmary as it resulted in a lower number of in-patients, with a subsequent loss of revenue for the institution.

Wishing to resolve this intractable problem, Messrs Meyrick and Meredith, secretaries of the two friendly societies, the Ancient Order of Foresters (Court Shakespeare) and the Manchester Unity of Oddfellows (Temple Lodge), who jointly formed the Bridgnorth Friendly Societies' Medical Association, attended the Infirmary's annual subscribers' meeting on 31 March 1914. Regretting that the 'three local doctors could not see their way to take service under the Insurance Act', they put forward the proposition that the Infirmary's Bye-Law No. 9, which required that the Honorary Medical Staff consist of three qualified practitioners, be amended to include the two panel doctors, Berry and Devonald. This proposition was immediately rejected upon a point of order by a certain Lieutenant-Colonel Cunliffe who appeared to be a stickler for the rules. A member of the Management Committee, he threatened to resign because such an amendment 'would lead to the forcible resignation – for it came to that – of those who had served faithfully for years'. With the threat of resignation by the medical staff now exposed, Dr Craig informed the meeting that:

> *if they* [the subscribers] *passed a resolution to admit the imported Insurance Act doctors the present staff were bound to resign by the rules of the* [BMA] *Ethical Committee in London. They had no option. There was no outcry* [from other doctors] *in any part of their district outside Bridgnorth. They were content to send the patients to receive the benefits of the Institute under the medical staff there, and the idea of putting on the Insurance Act doctors, because they were Insurance Act doctors, was ridiculed by other institutions.*[35]

Continuing, Dr Craig then gave 'particulars of enquiries', made by himself, of five hospitals where there had been no applications to increase the medical staff (Table 6).

Table 6. Dr Craig's report on five hospitals.

Hospital	Number of Hospital beds	Number of Doctors	Number of Panel Doctors	Number of Doctors on Hospital staff	Number of Panel Doctors on Hospital staff
Oswestry	17 + 2 cots	9	9	2	2
Salop Inf.	130	22	7	6	none
Malvern	24	24	23	5	5
Wolverhampton General	202	47	35	12	none
Stafford General	77	10	5	3	2

Source: *Bridgnorth Journal*, Saturday 4 April 1914, p. 5, col. 4, Dr Craig.

His arguments for not accepting the two panel doctors were, therefore, twofold: first, the alleged 'rules of the Ethical Committee in London', and second, that five hospitals had not received applications to increase their medical staff. Whether or not the ethical 'rules' of the BMA required doctors to resign from their posts is open to question. As for his enquiries, none, according to Craig, had received applications to increase their hospital staff. Ironically, of the five hospitals named, two were staffed entirely by panel doctors whilst the Stafford General Hospital had two panel doctors who worked alongside a non-panel doctor without, presumably, any censure upon either party. This suggests that all parties concerned were willing to work within the new health care system, unlike the Honorary Surgeons at the Bridgnorth Infirmary. As for the BMA, they withdrew their objection to the National Insurance Act following concessions from the Government. So too did the Shropshire and Mid-Wales branch of the BMA at their meeting on 6 January 1913 when it was agreed that they 'could not condemn those who were forced in self-preservation to go on the panel'.[36]

As a consequence, 111 doctors signed up with the Shropshire Insurance Committee thus breaking with the previous resolution not to enter into a contract with them. This was a contract that Doctors Craig, Padwick and Dickson chose to reject, hence the unsatisfactory situation that emerged in Bridgnorth and the subsequent action taken by the Shropshire Insurance Committee to 'import' the two panel doctors Berry and Devonald. Their arrival and subsequent appointment as MOs to the Friendly Societies Medical Association had precipitated the resignations of Doctors Craig, Padwick and Dickson from the Association; a threat that the Infirmary subscribers now faced if they voted to amend Bye-Law No. 9 to include Doctors Berry and Devonald. In the event, a long and 'useful discussion' took place where no vote was taken on an issue that was proving contentious. This decision to think things over rather than address the issue would create continuing problems, especially for the President, Mr W.H. Foster. At the annual meeting in March 1914, the President accepted Dr Craig's view of the medical staff's position with regard to the 'Ethical Committee in London' without reservation. However, the Revd A. Hodgson was more circumspect in what he had heard, as it seemed to him:

> *from what Dr. Craig had told them that it was the BMA that stood in the way. He rather thought that the BMA had shown its incapacity by the way in which it had treated the doctors. When the Insurance Act came into force the Association told them to stand out, and at the last minute stood on one side and allowed them to come in, and* **if** [emphasis supplied] *there were any rule that interfered concerning them* [the three honorary surgeons] *as supports of the Infirmary, he thought it should be set aside. Could they not prevail upon the three doctors to meet the other doctors in a reasonable, friendly and Christian spirit?*[37]

Others, including the President, regretted that the three doctors had not gone on the panel. Had they done so the President would not have found himself in a situation that 'had been the source of great anxiety to him for months past'. Whilst acknowledging the services of the three honorary medical staff, the President also 'sympathised very much with the panel doctors. He knew that they did their duty and devoted a great deal of their time to their work, and he would like to have seen some sort of recognition of their presence in the town'.[38]

That Bridgnorth's doctors, 'led by Dr. Craig', were opposed to the health insurance scheme has been alluded to elsewhere.[39] However, their opposition to the scheme does not fully explain why they were allegedly 'hostile' to the 'imported' panel doctors and 'boycotted them in every way'. Perhaps, the very fact that Berry and Devonald were 'imported' and therefore represented the new health care system was sufficient reason in itself to oppose their presence? A further consideration is money – or the lack of it – as Berry and Devonald reportedly engaged in private practice, thereby posing a threat to the respective livelihoods of Dr Craig and his colleagues who tenaciously held on to salaried posts in the community.

Such notions are speculative. As is the assumption that Dr Craig, as a Trustee and Honorary Surgeon to the Infirmary, was influential in impressing his views upon others in an era that was deferential to the medical profession and where junior medical colleagues were respectful of seniority. Hence, perhaps, the reluctance of many to challenge his threat of resignation and those of his colleagues should the subscribers vote to amend the rules and admit the 'imported Insurance Act doctors' to the Infirmary. By making his position and that of his colleagues known at the annual meeting in 1914, Dr Craig created a moral dilemma that would not easily be resolved. For the President, it was a problem that, in time, would lead him to threaten his resignation if the question of the panel doctors was not addressed in a positive and favourable manner.

Five months after the annual meeting, which was extensively reported in the *Bridgnorth Journal* for all to read, war suddenly erupted upon a nation that was ill-prepared for a lengthy battle. The onset of war brought yet more change at the Infirmary, when it became designated an Auxiliary Hospital. Out went the young nurse probationers to be replaced by women from the local Voluntary Aid Detachment (VAD) whose services came at no expense to the Infirmary. Referred to as 'VAD Nurses' in Infirmary reports, their presence allowed Matron Bailie to concentrate on her administrative tasks in an Infirmary where the reception and treatment of wounded military personnel, in addition to civilian patients, would bring demands previously not experienced.

In the wider community, war also brought bereavement, poverty and continuing dissatisfaction with the Infirmary Committee and the Honorary Surgeons who resolutely continued to bar the panel doctors from the institution; a stance that was unacceptable to many and one that would eventually be resolved, but not in a time of war.

8   War and the Peace Unfolded

We are living at a time, wrote the historian W.H. Dawson, *when days and weeks have the fullness and significance of years and decades. Who does not feel that since August 1914 England has in many ways broken with her past and entered an entirely new epoch in her history marked by transformations of every kind, so that when the day of peace arrives, be it soon or late, we shall be confronted at home by an altogether altered situation?*[1]

For Britain, the First World War commenced at 11 p.m. on Tuesday 4 August 1914 following Germany's violation of Belgium neutrality. This act of aggression against a weak but brave nation prompted tens of thousands of Belgian refugees to flee their country for England where the Central War Refugees' Committee was responsible for their dispersal throughout the country. Offers of hospitality were now required from various bodies, including private householders, that were facilitated in Bridgnorth by the local Belgian Refugees' Hospitality Committee.[2]

By early November there were some 450 Belgian refugees housed in Shropshire, including a contingent at Bridgnorth. By this time officialdom had become aware that many of them were 'suffering from phthisis [pulmonary tuberculosis], nervous shock [post-traumatic stress disorder], infectious diseases, epilepsy etc.'[3] In order to address this issue the Central War Refugees' Committee sent out requests to hospitals, including the Bridgnorth Infirmary, to receive cases for treatment, free of charge. This request was accommodated by the Infirmary Committee, in conjunction with the three honorary surgeons, who agreed that 'all suitable cases' would be admitted 'free of all charge, and without subscribers' tickets' to those refugees who were resident in the district.[4] How many sick refugees, if any, were treated at the Infirmary is not recorded but certain conditions, such as infectious diseases, including tuberculosis, as well as psychiatric illnesses were, historically, excluded from the Infirmary. As a consequence it is assumed that those persons presenting with an 'unsuitable' illness

113

would have been referred to a specialist institution (for example an infectious diseases hospital, a sanatorium or an asylum) for treatment elsewhere.

The onset of war also brought two further requests, both of which were acceded to by the Infirmary Committee. The first came from the War Office requesting that a ward be set aside for the reception of wounded soldiers whose maintenance would be derived from public funds. This request would ultimately require civilian patients to be accommodated in 'other rooms as Wards for the sick';[5] an arrangement that was thought, erroneously, to be temporary. The other request came from the British Red Cross Society which, in October 1914, had combined with the Order of St John to form the Joint War Committee under the Red Cross name and emblem. Both bodies were responsible for the raising and training of Voluntary Aid Detachment (VAD) units and in the staffing of auxiliary hospitals[6] which, in the following year of 1915, would include the Bridgnorth Infirmary where women VAD members would be admitted for practical experience in hospital work, at no expense to the Infirmary. Known collectively as VADs (but often referred to as 'nurses'), only 'selected members' would be admitted for work experience; an arrangement, made by the Infirmary Committee with Matron Bailie who, in September 1914, had enrolled with the Sheffield detachment of the British Red Cross with the rank of Matron. Matron Bailie's service with the British Red Cross, in addition to her role of Matron at the Infirmary, would include 'a considerable amount of secretarial and Quartermaster's work'[7] that would become excessive during the course of the war.

If the Infirmary staff were preparing for what lay ahead so too was the local populace, for amongst those responding to the call to 'BE A PATRIOT'[8] were the boys of the Bridgnorth Baden-Powell Scouts Association, who were mobilised to guard Government telegraph lines as far afield as Morville, Ludlow and Bewdley. Bereft of decent boots and lacking overcoats, the scouts were subsequently provided with both by Mr W.H. Foster of Apley following an appeal to 'generous friends'. With an immediate increase in the price of foodstuffs the call to 'think of others more than usual' was also responded to with the suggestion that a food depot be established, especially for the town's 'poorer neighbours' who, with the rest of Britain's working class families, often lived below the poverty line.

The onset of war also had immediate effects upon trade and industry as wholesale merchants and manufacturers curtailed credit. Bridgnorthians were therefore urged to shop locally and pay for their acquisitions in cash, rather than use credit, if shopkeepers were to remain solvent and avoid the spectre of closure with subsequent unemployment for themselves and their staff. There was also 'industrial distress' at Bridgnorth's principal factory, Southwell's Carpet Manufactory, where 'considerable and immediate relief was required' by September 1914. A month previously:

There were 62 men whose average wages … were 24/3 per week which were now reduced to 11/4 and would further be reduced. There were also 47 girls and women whose average wages had been reduced from 11/11 to 4/4½ and 46 others from 14/6 to 4/3½ per week. This employment will probably have to be still further reduced. The wages of the employees in the Worsted Spinning Works had been reduced from 40 to 10 per cent'.[9]

This pending privation amongst Bridgnorth's working poor, some of whom were already unemployed, was addressed by a 'private scheme' to provide some employment 'especially for the men'. For those unemployed women, a 'Work Room' would be established at St Mary's Parish Rooms in Low Town, where 'relief work' entailed making garments from material provided by Queen Mary's Needlework Fund, for distribution among the troops and hospitals. Organised primarily by the Bridgnorth Women's Suffrage Society, a non-militant and apolitical group separate from the Pankhurst's suffragette movement, the unemployed women would receive a token sum of money derived from a government grant.[10] A further organisation that was supportive of women, and particularly pregnant women (who, as maternity cases, were also excluded from the Infirmary), was the recently formed Bridgnorth and District Nursing Association. Affiliated with Queen Victoria's Jubilee Institute for Nurses and the Shropshire Nursing Federation, the sole nurse, who would be joined by another in 1917, was described as 'a fully qualified general and midwifery County Council district nurse'.[11] Employed to provide a maternal, infant and school welfare service, her work was considered to be of 'National importance' in safeguarding the well-being of infants and children (and therefore the nation) during a time of war.

The onset of war also brought opportunities for other women when the Infirmary Committee agreed to the formation of a Ladies' Committee. Their first President was a Mrs Evelyn Gilroy of Dallicott House, near Claverley, who is noted for being the first woman elected to the Infirmary's Committee of Management (1915) and later (1917) as a member of the House Committee. This same year of 1917 also saw two other women elected to the Committee of Management, namely: Mrs E.T. Crook (now President of the Ladies' Committee) and the Hon. Mrs M. Hamilton-Russell, who was also elected to the House Committee.

As a committee of ladies their energies and organisational abilities soon came to the fore with the immediate introduction of: a 'Linen Guild' that provided household linens and various garments for patients from a list drawn up by Matron Bailie; a 'Hamper Scheme' which entailed individuals and parishes providing weekly hampers of seasonal foodstuffs, including groceries, to supplement the diets of patients and staff alike; and a panel of 'Lady Visitors', two of whom would visit patients on a monthly basis. A year later (1915) the Ladies' Committee also undertook responsibility for the Hospital Saturday collections that extended beyond the town to country parishes and collections from miners at collieries in Highley, Kinlet and Billingsley. The object of all these activities was primarily to reduce the Infirmary's housekeeping expenditure, which grew throughout the war, whilst income from other sources fluctuated, except for subscriptions – the 'mainstay' of the Infirmary – that rose by a few pounds (Table 7).

Table 7. Housekeeping expenditure and various receipts: 1915–1918

Year	1915	1916	1917	1918
Housekeeping expenses	£416 1s 10d	£640 1s 2d	£986 5s 4d	£1035 0s 4d
Receipts	-	-	-	-
Subscriptions	£300 2s 0d	£300 17s 6d	£305 15s 0d	£308 18s 0d
Provident Members	£8 8s 5d	£7 1s 5d	£5 17s 4d	£5 1s 0d
Church Collections	£121 4s 1d	£103 6s 10d	£ 98 0s 10d	£116 1s 10d
Hospital Saturday	£106 0s 5d	£ 80 10s 1d	£120 17s 1d	£137 18s 11d

Source: Bridgnorth Hospital Records, Bridgnorth Infirmary Report Book 1915–1918.

Meanwhile, in February 1915, continuing dissatisfaction with the 'existing conditions' at the Infirmary was being expressed, but not elaborated upon, by the local branch of the Manchester Unity of Oddfellows. A few weeks later, the Guardians of the Bridgnorth Union were also complaining that the Workhouse Infirmary had become the 'dumping ground for all the doctor's cases'. Couldn't the Bridgnorth Infirmary take a particular case under discussion? 'Yes' was the reply, providing the applicant came with 'notes' and was willing to 'voluntarily relinquish his claim [to National Insurance benefit] and give it to the institution'.[12] The grumblings of both these organisations, each of whom had either access to or representatives on the Infirmary's Committee of Management, were not raised at the annual meeting that took place on 10 March 1915. Indeed, the only reference to the National Insurance Act came from Dr Padwick, whose annual report for 1914 identified a decrease in the number of outpatients, which was attributed, in part, to the Act 'which would take off many of the people who came … with minor ailments'.[13]

Seven days later, on Wednesday 17 March 1915, concerns at the Infirmary shifted towards other matters when the institution officially became an Auxiliary Hospital, with the arrival of its first contingent of 15 wounded soldiers. For some of the wounded, who had experienced the first episode of trench warfare at the battle of Neuve Chapelle (10–13 March), their recollections of war would 'not be easily effaced'. Their journey had also been long and arduous. Having been brought from France, the wounded arrived at Southampton docks on the morning of Tuesday 16 March, from whence they were transported in an ambulance train to the railhead at Shrewsbury. Arriving in the early hours of Wednesday morning, they were met by volunteers in five private cars from Bridgnorth and transported to the Infirmary where they arrived at 'about a quarter to 5 a.m., tired out by [a] long journey'[14] of some 20 hours from the docks at Southampton.

That private cars were used to convey the wounded is explained by an absence of ambulances in the town – a situation that was not peculiar to Bridgnorth, as it was said by Mr William Swire, County Director of the British Red Cross Society, that there were no ambulances in the County in the 'first days' of the war; a problem that would not be resolved until private individuals donated ambulances to the cause.[15] Known as 'Red Cross Motor Ambulances', none, it would seem, were routinely available in Bridgnorth, leaving the local VAD (St John) Ambulance Corps reliant upon private vehicles that included motor vans and horse drays.

Although the Severn Valley Railway and its station at Bridgnorth had opened in 1862, the ambulance train came no further than the junction at Buildwas; hence the journey to Shrewsbury to collect the wounded men who frequently arrived in the early hours of a morning. This logistical problem had repercussions for Matron Bailie and the local Ambulance Corps, as Matron, who received notice of pending arrivals from the War Office had, in some instances, only an hour-and-a-half's notice to summon and dispatch the volunteers to Shrewsbury.[16] This problem, however, was resolved on 16 September 1916 when the *Bridgnorth Journal* reported that an ambulance train had arrived at Bridgnorth station with 22 cases, half of whom were 'cot cases', for conveying to the Infirmary by a 'Red Cross Motor Ambulance and vans'. The largest batch of men to arrive to date, the conveyance of these more seriously wounded men would, in future days and months, put the local Ambulance Corps 'to the test' with the arrival of yet more 'cot cases' whose transportation by 'improvised volunteer ambulance waggons'[17] created concern at the Infirmary. This led the honorary secretary to write to the leader of the VAD Ambulance Corps and others, requesting that the private vehicles be made more suitable for ambulance work, the cost of which would have to be met by the owner.[18]

Of the wounded and invalided servicemen, nothing is known of them or their injuries. Their presence, however, was acknowledged by the raising of the Union flag upon the Infirmary's flagpole in recognition of their valour. Fed, clothed, entertained and provided with gifts (including tobacco, puzzles and books), the men, upon their discharge, wrote letters of 'gratitude' for the treatments they had received, whilst one was reported as saying that he thought they were treated 'a good too well'.[19] As for the maintenance of the military personnel, this had been agreed in 1914 when the

Infirmary Committee accepted a War Office grant at a daily rate of 3/- to 3/6 for each serviceman whilst at the Infirmary. Ultimately, this capitation grant neither wholly reflected the increasing price of foodstuffs nor the Infirmary's role as an Auxiliary Hospital in receiving cases direct from ambulance trains. From a financial perspective, the Red Cross in Shropshire categorised Auxiliary Hospitals as either 'A' or 'B'. Those classed as 'A' received cases direct from ambulance trains and received '3/6 per head, per diem if their monthly account showed that they had earned it'. Those hospitals classed as 'B', which took the 'more convalescent cases', such as the Worfield 'Auxiliary Home Hospital', received up to 3/- per head, per diem.[20]

The remittance came from the War Office, which was informed, through returns on activity at Bridgnorth, by Matron Bailie. Although the Infirmary received cases direct from ambulance trains (from September 1916 onwards), the grant suggests that there was a preponderance of invalided personnel (rather than the more seriously wounded) and therefore the Infirmary had not 'earned' the higher rate of compensation. Nevertheless, there were those in the community who, by the end of the war, were claiming that the Infirmary had made a 'very handsome profit out of the Government'.[21] This assertion was dispelled at the Infirmary's annual meeting in April 1918, when it was revealed that the real cost of maintenance for each military personnel on a daily basis was 4/3 and not the previously agreed 3/- to 3/6. This same meeting also referred to the number of beds, which pre-war had consisted of 20 beds and two cots. By 1918 there were said to be 40 beds, two-thirds of which were given up to military personnel, whilst the remaining one-third were occupied by civilians, of whom two-thirds were paying patients. This meeting also referred to the continuing difficulties over the exclusion of the panel doctors and the unwillingness of the Committee to alter its stance on the matter. This was a problem that was now said to be 'insuperable' and one that was about to be raised yet again. Present at the meeting was Mr Alfred Edge, an officer of the Friendly Societies' Medical Association and Mayor of Bridgnorth, who rose to address the gathering. Choosing his words carefully he suggested that there was a need to make:

> a truce ... between the doctors living in our midst. He knew that it was a vexed question, but it seemed deplorable that there should be differences, and a want of unanimity between doctors when it concerned an institution that had done so much good. He knew that it was felt very keenly by people amongst the working classes outside. He heard complaints and he heard suggestions ... could the committee bridge this gulf, if so it would not only be a great help to that institution but a benefit to humanity.[22]

In response, the President stated that he 'sympathised' with the Mayor's remarks. He was also glad that he had raised the question, for 'this was a time when all should be working together, and he would be glad if something could be done to meet this difficulty which was always before them';[23] a plea that fell on deaf ears.

If there were those in the community who thought that the onset of war might have engendered a more collaborative approach amongst Bridgnorth's doctors, they were mistaken – even when it became apparent that some would leave for service with the Royal Army Medical Corps (RAMC). The first doctor to resign was the Infirmary's house-surgeon, Mr C.C. Court, who was the last house-surgeon to be employed at the Infirmary. He gave two months' notice in July 1914, but no replacement could be found as many doctors, and nurses, were signing up for service at the 'Front' or in base hospitals. It also transpired that even if a junior doctor had been found there were insufficient monies in the coffers to employ one, which left Matron Bailie responsible for attending to the Provident Members whilst the honorary surgeons attended to the remaining patients.

The second doctor to join the RAMC was Dr Devonald, who was commissioned on 1 April 1915 as a Surgeon-Lieutenant with the Surrey Yeomanry's 83rd Field Ambulance, Territorial Forces. Twenty-six days later he was in France where, on 22 June 1915, he was recommended for his gallant and distinguished service in the field.[24] Soon to follow in his footsteps was Dr Padwick who, since 1910, had been an elected Bridgnorth Corporation Councillor for East Ward. By October 1915 he had expressed his willingness to be nominated as Mayor of Bridgnorth: a nomination from which he withdrew when his offer of military service was accepted on 1 December 1915 as a Second Lieutenant in the RAMC. Married in 1911 to a granddaughter of Mr T. Martin Southwell, Dr Padwick returned to Bridgnorth at the end of the war only to find continuing problems at the Infirmary. Allegedly sympathetic towards the panel doctors, Dr Padwick resigned from all his medical posts, including that of honorary surgeon to the Infirmary, upon leaving the town at the end of 1918 to recommence a life elsewhere.

Meanwhile, the departure of these medical men now left their respective colleagues with a heavy workload, the strain of which bore down upon them during a war that was neither short nor glorious. This fact was recognised by Messrs Enoch Sarjeant and Alfred Edge, officers of the Friendly Societies' Medical Association, when Dr Berry took on the whole of Dr Devonald's practice which, apparently, now saw him with a caseload of some 3,000 patients in addition to others, including private patients. For Mr Sarjeant, he:

> *personally felt that very much credit was due to Dr. Berry in those circumstances (Hear, hear). It had been a very great strain upon him undoubtedly both as regards his physical health and professional abilities, but he had won the esteem of all connected with the Association.*[25]

These sentiments were shared by Mr Edge who also thought that 'Dr. Berry had done nobly in the circumstances [for] his many other patients connected with other phases of his work had not hindered him from fulfilling his obligations to the Association [that had been tendered with] courtesy and attention'.[26] In spite of all these pressures, Dr Berry was still willing for the Association to put his name forward to the Infirmary's Committee of Management to allow him to enter the premises; an annual request that was denied on each and every occasion throughout the war, even though Dr Craig admitted that he and Dr Dickson had:

> *tried to do all that they could, and he did not disguise the fact that they missed a house surgeon very much, and also the services of Mr. Padwick one of the honorary surgeons. It was not so much the visiting in the town, but the tie had been very great of a morning especially when there was a member of soldiers there. It had been a great strain.*[27]

Now obliged to visit the Infirmary almost daily, Doctors Craig and Dickson continued to oppose the presence of Dr Berry who, in 1916, purchased the 'The Grove', a 'Desirable Freehold Residence' in West Castle Street that stood in its own grounds with stabling and a motor house.[28] The property had previously been in the ownership of Mrs Julie Minna Hewett who, having died in October 1915, had survived her late husband, Mr Frank William Hewett, by four years. The younger son of a baronet, Mr Hewett first came to Bridgnorth as an assistant civil engineer on the Severn Valley Railway in 1858. Returning to Bridgnorth in 1880 to reside permanently in the town, he first became a member of the Infirmary Committee on 17 June 1882, and subsequently the honorary treasurer in 1893; a post that he retained until his 90th year in 1910.[29] Mr Hewett was highly regarded by those at the Infirmary, and a subscription was raised to provide a permanent record of his public service, which came in the form of a brass plaque. Unlike other plaques, portraits, tablets and other memorabilia, this plaque is still retained at the Infirmary in the 1896 building and reads:

> In the memory of Frank William Hewett, of The Grove, Bridgnorth, who died October 22nd, 1911, and was for the last 30 years of his life deeply interested in the Infirmary and devoted his time and energy to its welfare. A special fund was invested and the tablet was placed by subscribers and other friends in appreciation of his long and faithful services, July, 1912.

By 1917, the war was taking its toll on many in the community. To alleviate unemployment amongst men and women, the Town Council had endeavoured to bring munitions work to Bridgnorth, but to no avail. There were also problems for Messrs

Wardle & Company, textile printers of Pale Meadow Mills in Low Town who, despite the economic difficulties of the time, were still functioning as a business. The threat of closure, however, loomed large as the company's 38-year-old departmental manager was being called up under the Military Service Act. Categorised as Class A and therefore fit for general service, his conscription would lead to the closure of the firm. Arriving in Bridgnorth to seek an 'absolute exemption' from military service for his manager was Major Wardle, who appeared before a local tribunal to press his case for the firm's survival. Held in the Town Hall, the tribunal responded with a reprieve of three months.[30] The result doubtless raised uncertainties for the departmental manager whilst giving little satisfaction to Major Wardle, who would have to return to Bridgnorth to plead his case again if the company was to remain viable.

At the Infirmary things were little better, as inflation ate into receipts and effected the ever-increasing costs of expenditure. The latter was made more exceptional by the repair of a ward ceiling that had fallen in, and 'the heavy cost of darkening the windows' from a war in the air that did not materialise above the skies of Bridgnorth. In an effort to reduce some costs the annual report was now reduced from 16 to 12 pages and printed without a front cover; a policy that continued until 1920 when the records of the Infirmary Report Book ceased. Meanwhile, by the year of 1917, Matron Bailie's administrative work had increased to such an extent that the Infirmary Committee agreed to her being relieved 'of the excessive amount of work thrown upon her hands in filling up [sic] forms, making returns etc., in accordance with the War Office regulations'.[31] To ease her burden, the Committee appointed a Mrs Wood (Commandant of Bridgnorth's women VADs, and district organiser of the National Egg Collection scheme) as Quartermaster and therefore responsible for the provision's store, whilst Miss Maud Bate was appointed as the clerical assistant.

The Ladies' Committee was also facing difficulties, as the increase in the cost of materials had affected the quality and number of items donated to the Linen Guild (which, in 1917, had been reduced to 269 items compared with 439 items in the previous year). Similarly, the Hamper Scheme was also foundering due to the high price of foodstuffs. This saw some members of the local gentry providing hampers but not the country parishes who 'had found it impossible to provide for their transit to and from the country'[32] (suggesting that fuel was rationed and in short supply). There were, however, 'large farmers' in the rural district who were, reputedly, 'having a good time now'.[33] As 'large employers of labour', the farmers contributed to the National Insurance scheme and therefore saw little reason to subscribe to the Infirmary, particularly as there were difficulties over panel patients and their attending doctors being refused access to the institution. This continuing problem now saw the 75-year-old Revd Prebendary John Wright, Honorary Secretary to the Infirmary for 35 years, resign his post on 15 December 1917, owing to a 'difference of opinion, which appeared to be vital, between the Committee and myself'.[34] This enigmatic remark leaves us in a quandary: did he support the inclusion of the panel doctors or did he not? One suspects that as a Christian gentleman he wished the situation to be resolved in line with the President's wishes: that the panel doctors should be accepted by the Infirmary Committee. His resignation now prompted the appointment of Lieutenant-Colonel Harold Echalaz Welch, DSO and Bar, a professional soldier who had accepted the post of assistant secretary in 1914. A resident of 'Cantreyn' (a property in the Parish of Astley Abbotts, which he had inherited from his grandfather), Harold Welch would die in action near Amiens on 29 March 1918.[35] Aged 39, he left behind a widow and yet a further vacancy at the Infirmary where his loss was deeply regretted. A further death, but in retirement, was that of Dr William Thursfield, MD, who had left Bridgnorth in 1911 to reside with his family in Jamaica. Dying in his 80th year on 22 April 1918, Dr Thursfield was the fourth and last Consulting Physician of a generation[36] to be appointed to the Infirmary, until 1934 (by which time several honorary consultants from the Wolverhampton General Hospital had been invited to attend the Infirmary).

If the death of Dr Thursfield was an end of an era, so too was the cessation of the 'Great War', that occurred at the 11th hour on the 11th day of the 11th month in 1918. However, another four months would elapse before the Infirmary resumed its civilian status in March 1919, with 27 disabled soldiers and six pensioners still maintained at the expense of the Ministry of Pensions in 1920.

As an Auxiliary Hospital, no fewer than 787 soldiers and naval personnel had passed through its doors at a cost to the public purse of £4,014 10s (Table 8).

Table 8. Bridgnorth Auxiliary Hospital, March 1915 – March 1919.

Year	Military Patients	Disabled Soldiers	Discharged Soldiers	War Office Maintenance £ s d
1915	69			£254 11s 0d
1916	139			£522 18s 0d
1917	240			£1252 12s 0d
1918	255		11	£1635 2s 0d
1919	84	35		£349 7s 0d
Total	787	35	11	£4014 10s 0d

Source: Bridgnorth Hospital Records, *Bridgnorth Infirmary Report Book 1915–1919*, Surgical Reports and Revenue Accounts (receipts).

With the withdrawal of the War Office capitation grant, the Infirmary Committee was now reduced to an annual income of £900, which in reality required £1500 if the

Infirmary was to remain a viable concern. What was needed were more subscribers, including farmers, but before that could happen the issue surrounding the panel doctors had to be addressed, particularly as Dr Devonald had returned to the town after his service with the RAMC. His return now appears to have prompted rumours in the town that Dr Berry was about to leave, which was refuted when the editor of the *Bridgnorth Journal* printed a disclaimer at the request of Dr Berry.

At the Infirmary's annual meeting on Wednesday 19 March 1919, the President, Mr W.H. Foster, made his position clear when he addressed the gathering. Recognising the 'changed circumstances of the times', and doubtless driven by exasperation, his remarks, combined with those of Mr Edge (now President of the Friendly Societies' Medical Association) proved to be a turning point, especially when Mr Foster declared that:

> *Certain things had given him a great deal of anxiety, a great amount of worry, and a great amount of dread, for since their rules and bye-laws were drawn up* [in 1897 and 1898 respectively] *things had changed. The Infirmary should be more representative. He had done all that he could to bring about that result, but with no effect. They wished to see the best of their working classes treated in this hospital – (Hear, hear) – and his sympathy was with those who wished to be treated there by their own medical attendants. He thought he should mention this, for there might be a time when he would have to resign if a course were adopted he could not approve of. It was a subject that would have to be settled sooner or later. They wanted to do their best for this hospital, they wanted to discourage all antagonism of any sort, and they wanted to deal with certain patients, and although he accepted the office* [of President] *now it would depend to a certain extent on how these matters were settled whether he continued in office.*[37]

With this threat of resignation hanging in the air, the President now invited Mr Edge to take the floor. Mr Edge suggested that, as Dr Padwick had left the town, a vacancy now existed among the medical staff (which, under the rules, should consist of three doctors). He therefore wished 'to move a resolution to the effect that the Committee be asked to place Dr. Devonald's name on the honorary medical staff'; a move that was fully endorsed by the President. However, as on a previous occasion, it was Lieutenant-Colonel Cunliffe who rose to question procedural matters, whilst asserting that the motion was 'out of order' and *ultra vires* (beyond legal authority). He continued by stating that he would not be dictated to (one wonders by whom: Mr Edge, the President?), as it was up to the elected 'General Committee ... to do the best that they could in their own judgement'. Furthermore 'until their own honorary medical staff told him they submitted to the addition of this other doctor to the roll he refused to move a step forward to [Dr Devonald] being elected'[38] and in saying, let another 'cat out of the bag'! Retaining his composure, Mr Edge reminded those present that:

> The Committee had declined to put Dr. Berry's name on the list, and now that Dr. Devonald applied the only course was to bring the matter forward, as he had done, if that institution was to do work it was built for. He would like to say in defence of his own position, he was not entirely unrepresentative. He knew that he represented the friendly societies and the insured patients of the town and district, and he represented also a large body of public opinion, which had expressed itself forcibly and audibly, that this matter should be settled'.[39]

Predictably, nothing was settled at this meeting. There was, however, some progress as Mr Edge was unexpectedly appointed to the committee; a move that pleased the Friendly Societies' Medical Association who were now placed, through the appointment of Mr Edge, to prosecute the matter further. Another development was a private remark, made by an Infirmary Committee member, who 'felt sure that at the next meeting of the Committee the problem would be solved, and their wishes assented to'.[40] The wish was partially fulfilled when, later in the year, a number of beds were allocated for the use of insured patients who were still denied the attendance of their panel doctors. Meanwhile, the changing social order had brought forth a series of letters – the first of their kind – from a local resident, Mr Thomas R. Oakley, who considered it unjust that the Infirmary should refuse those in 'the community the privileges enjoyed by patients of private doctors' for, as he had previously remarked, 'Panel patients were as human as private ones'.[41]

As for Matron Bailie, recognition came for her long hours of service during the war when she was awarded the Royal Red Cross (1st Class) on 1 August 1919. It was a decoration that she 'received at the hands' of King George V on 4 December 1920[42] by which time Miss Bailie had given notice to resign her post after 26 years' service. Unlike with the resignation of Miss Hadfield in 1894, there is no mention in the local paper of a testimonial being raised to provide a parting gift, or a report on her leaving, other than that the members of the Infirmary Committee had 'suitably recognised her services' and 'passed a most unanimous vote of thanks to her for the great care and diligence she had given to her patients'.[43] Aged about 60 years, Miss Bailie must have been prompted to resign by the abysmal staffing arrangements at the Infirmary where it was reported that obtaining 'both nursing and domestic staff' was 'almost impossible'.[44] As a consequence Miss Bailie was reportedly left with one cook and a girl of 16 years to assist her in a hospital that nearly closed for lack of staff. This situation was said to be unknown to the general public, and it was one that was only rescued by the reintroduction of the VADs, whose presence prevented its closure.[45] Further progress came, however, with the appointment of a new matron by the name of Miss M.E. Dickenson (or Dickinson) in early February 1921. Previously of the Bolton Infirmary, Miss Dickenson came with 'great experience' and 'excellent credentials'. She was also credited with knowing 'her duties well', and as being someone 'who could train probationers to be excellent nurses[46] in an institution that remained reliant on voluntary helpers as late as 1923 due to a continuing shortage of nurses and domestic staff.

There also remained the nagging question of who should be appointed as the third member of the honorary medical staff at the Infirmary. The decision appears to have been deferred until 1922 when Dr E.L.N. Rhodes, the elder son of the late Dr William Rhodes, was appointed to the post having returned to Bridgnorth – (at a date unknown) after service with the RAMC. With a local man in place rather than an 'imported' panel doctor, the Infirmary Committee now made arrangements for Doctors Berry and Devonald to admit their private patients to private wards and therefore attend all their patients – both panel and private – at the Infirmary; an arrangement that had taken nine years to accomplish due, finally, to the continuing efforts of Mr Edge. Others had also made their opinions known, including the Bridgnorth Branch of the National Farmers Union whose members were now willing to subscribe to the Infirmary where subscriptions were falling, expenditure increasing and where financial uncertainty existed. This financial anxiety would continue until October 1927 when a weekly contribution scheme of 1d was introduced that no longer required the working classes to search out a 'ticket' or hand over their National Insurance benefits to the Infirmary. This was based on a scheme employed at the Wolverhampton General Hospital, whose Governor, Mr Harper, was invited to address a public meeting in Bridgnorth at which he stressed the importance of involving working men in the scheme and the necessity of placing someone they trusted on the Infirmary's Board of Management.[47] This advice was taken and led to a greater co-operation between the Wolverhampton General Hospital and the Infirmary, which would prove mutually beneficial to both parties, including patients, and which it was hoped would lead to more prosperous days ahead.

Meanwhile, Dr Berry who, by comparison to Dr Devonald, led a comparatively private life during his time in Bridgnorth, sold his practice to Dr James Lewis Lloyd Jones in 1926 upon departing for Alverstoke in Hampshire where he continued to practice medicine. Of Dr Devonald's time in Bridgnorth, a little more is known before he too departed from the town in 1927. Returning to Bridgnorth as a married man in 1920, he was appointed as the Regimental Medical Officer to the 4th Battalion KSLI, Territorial Force. This same year also saw him actively engaged as a founding member of the Bridgnorth and District Lawn Tennis Club; assisting with the reformation of the Bridgnorth Golf Club and, on 1 November, becoming an elected Town Councillor for Morfe Ward. By 1925 he was lecturing to the St John Ambulance Association whose members, at that time, included railwaymen, policemen and scouts. He therefore followed in the footsteps of Dr Wilfred Watkins-Pitchford who had been appointed to the Infirmary as a house-surgeon in 1894 and who, in 1895, had introduced a series of separate lectures to the men and women of the Association. After a distinguished medical career in South Africa[48] Dr Watkins-Pitchford returned to Bridgnorth in 1926 where, in retirement, he interested himself in the Infirmary before becoming a noted local historian and the founding President of the Bridgnorth and District Historical Society, during which time he also served as a magistrate on the Borough Bench.

The respective departures of Doctors Berry and Devonald went without comment in the local press. Likewise, they too remained silent on the difficulties they had encountered in a town where their presence, combined with their professional abilities, were welcomed by the 'working poor' and respected by others, including the President whose sense of social justice for a 'more representative' Infirmary eventually prevailed. Living to see the day, Mr W.H. Foster died on 9 March 1924 having succumbed to bronchial pneumonia after a short illness. His death brought to an end yet another era at the Bridgnorth and South Shropshire Infirmary where, on 9 April, his son and heir, Major Arthur William Foster, MC, succeeded him. A veteran of the First World War, like others of his generation, he had sustained a severe wound that in his case required the amputation of a leg in May 1915. As heir to the Apley Estate, Major Foster would be the third and last representative of that family to become the Infirmary's President. His resignation also brought to an end the Infirmary's association with the Apley Estate whose owners, the Whitmores and then the Fosters, had provided land upon which the two Infirmaries were built. As President, Major A.W. Foster would also preside over further developments at the Infirmary and, indeed, its demise as a voluntary hospital when, in 1948, it became a public body.

Since the inaugural meeting on 29 November 1832 up until 5 July 1948 the two Infirmaries were built and maintained by voluntary effort. It was an era of philanthropy and the private interests of individuals whose purpose, throughout the years, was the provision of 'medical and surgical relief to the labouring population' (later referred to as the 'working classes'). That prejudices arose in the late 1830s, and again with the introduction of the National Insurance Act of 1911, was unfortunate, for both episodes challenged, in their respective ways, the founding principles of the Infirmary and, as we have seen, took years rather than months to resolve. Those developments that occurred were driven, often belatedly, by government policies and advances in the medical sciences and associated technologies that, by default, created a demand from patients whose numbers grew exponentially over a period of 112 years. Throughout this time, the lack of monies to upgrade the Infirmary and sustain a service remained a constant concern for those who were charged with administering an institution that was totally dependent upon charitable giving. Criticised from time to time by some in the community who thought the Infirmary could be better managed, the administrators and doctors, without exception, gave of their time and expertise, free of charge, in order to maintain a medical service for which demand frequently outstripped supply. It was a demand that would continue unabated with the introduction of the National Health Service on 5 July 1948, and one for which money remains, to this day, finite. This fact was well known and frequently experienced by those in previous times who founded and perpetuated, with difficulty, a voluntary hospital and charitable institution that, in 1995, was renamed the Bridgnorth Hospital. For those of a certain age, the Bridgnorth Hospital continues to be known, with affection, as 'the Infirmary', whose purpose many in the community, past and present, have valued, and whose presence they have therefore fought to continue; a presence that was established by James Milman Coley, Surgeon and Physician of Bridgnorth, whose name and achievements remain unrecognised and clouded in history.

Epilogue

THE final decades of the Infirmary as a charitable institution would be presided over by Major Foster who, as heir to the Apley Estate, would, as custom dictated, be 'elected' to the unenviable position of President – for this role was not, and never had been, a sinecure!

Throughout the decades, however, there were able men who were willing to support the various presidents. One such person in 1924 was an energetic 67-year-old by the name of Mr A.J. Buston of Astbury Hall, who had made his fortune as a cotton broker. As a trustee and benefactor he also brought to the Infirmary his drive and business acumen, which appears to have been exhibited with aplomb and strategic thinking until his death in 1937 when it was remarked that he would be 'almost impossible to replace'.[1] A future chairman of two building committees, he not only called upon the clergy to exchange their pulpits with the aim of seeing who could raise the most offertories towards the Hospital Sunday Fund but also encouraged the bequeathing of legacies which resulted in a specific bequest of £1,500 for an 'Accident Ward'. Opened in June 1926 to accommodate the increasing number of 'motor casualties' this new development had financial implications for the Infirmary, as treatment costs were frequently not met by the patients – many of whom were not local – leaving the Infirmary to 'bear the remainder of the debt',[2] which increased annually (as did the overall debt of the Infirmary). This financial situation was exemplified by the President at an annual meeting in April 1928 when he stated: 'How to make both ends meet is a yearly anxiety to the Committee, and a deficit has yet to be wiped out'. He later added that: 'If everything at the Infirmary is to be kept running efficiently, and in an up-to-date fashion, it is imperative that every person in this District should subscribe according to their means'.[3]

These pleas to the wider public for greater financial support in the form of voluntary subscriptions, donations and legacies had been a feature of the Infirmary since its inception, and would continue to be throughout the 1920s and '30s – even when the nation was beset by a general depression and mass unemployment that was epitomised by 'life on the dole'.

In Bridgnorth these same interwar years also saw the population declining, high rents for housing and a depression in trade and agriculture taking hold in the wider community where businesses and estates reduced their staffing levels with subsequent unemployment leading to fewer donations and subscriptions to the Infirmary. It was also recognised by Mr Buston and others that the 32-bed Infirmary, with its lack of facilities and modern equipment,[4] was insufficient to meet the needs of the local population. As a result it had been observed that many people in the town and district were using the Wolverhampton General Hospital whose facilities included access to specialist medical men. None, however, attended the Infirmary where three of Bridgnorth's general practitioners continued to provide a medical and surgical service. Efforts were now made to address the Infirmary's shortcomings, including its lack of subscribers; hence the approach, as previously mentioned, to the Governor of the Wolverhampton General Hospital and the introduction in 1927 of the Weekly Hospital Contributory Scheme which became the chief source of income over the ensuing years. The scheme, however, did not include annual subscribers – those who could afford a lump sum – all of whom were urged to give as much as possible, whilst appeals to non-subscribers to join the Infirmary often met with little success.

This same year of 1927 also saw the Governor of the Wolverhampton General Hospital appointed as a Vice-President of the Infirmary, whilst two specialist medical men – an 'Honorary Electrologist and Radiologist' (the Infirmary had purchased an X-Ray machine that was proving expensive to run and maintain) and an 'Honorary Pathologist' – were included on the Infirmary's Board of Management. This new development also included a reciprocal arrangement between the two hospitals, which permitted the referral of patients in Bridgnorth for treatment, free of charge, at Wolverhampton. Meanwhile, patients from Wolverhampton, whose hospital was 'always full', could be transferred to the Infirmary – space permitting – for which the Board would receive a weekly payment that would assist in reducing their 'overhead charges'.[5] By 1934 several other specialist medical men from Wolverhampton had joined the Infirmary as Honorary Consultants.[6] This would lead to patients in Bridgnorth also being referred to specialist hospitals, including the Wolverhampton Hospital for Women and the Wolverhampton and Midland Counties Eye Infirmary.

A further shortcoming was the need, often raised by Mr Buston, to alter and extend the Infirmary so that facilities might be improved for both patients and staff alike. As a consequence three major developments occurred during the interwar years – all of which would require funding. As with past and future developments at the Infirmary, appeals by the President to the public for donations now took place, as did the forming of a building committee and a subcommittee with the specific purpose of raising funds.

The first development that came was the opening of two 'new wings' on 6 December 1928, at a final cost of £3,120. Included amongst the alterations was the introduction of an operating suite. Originally just one room, this specialised facility now had an operating theatre with an integral 'sterilising and anaesthetic room [and a] robing room for surgeons',[7] all of which would later require a specialised nurse (the theatre sister) to oversee the smooth running of the suite. The old operating theatre now became an obstetric theatre for fee-paying maternity cases whose exclusion from the Infirmary had ceased in 1922. Registered by the Shropshire County Council on 27 February 1928 (under the Midwives and Maternity Homes Act of 1926), the Infirmary benefited financially from the increasing number of attending women, as did the medical fraternity with the increasing medicalisation of maternity cases. Seven Caesarian sections had been undertaken in 1924 during a six-month period without any fatalities. There were also four additional bedrooms to accommodate the residential nurses and staff that were said to number 12 in total. Other alterations included a new (and fifth) private ward, whilst a significant development was the introduction of electricity throughout the building (a utility that first came to Bridgnorth on 6 November 1928), thus enabling the Infirmary and the town access to the 'modern power'.[8]

The second major development – first mooted by Mr Buston in 1930 – was the need for a designated children's ward and a large maternity ward. With an estimate for the proposed build, including equipment, of £3,900, and only £1,000 raised by 1933, the management committee deferred the building of the children's ward, deciding instead to build a two-storey maternity block from which income was assured! Opened on the 27 September 1934, the 'Maternity Wing' with its fashionable 'glass-covered veranda facing south'[9] had all the necessary facilities, including a labour ward, a nursery, a six-bed public ward, two private wards and, on the upper floor, three bedrooms and a sitting room to accommodate some of the nursing staff. This ambitious development on land donated by Major Foster resulted in a deficit of £1,400, which was eventually reduced in 1937 following a bequest of £1,000 from the executors of the estate of the late Mr Buston (who, in 1934, had previously donated £500 towards the build in memory of his wife).

Notwithstanding such financial difficulties, the third major development was the structural alterations and improvements to the 'Service Block', at an estimated cost of £2,500, where no improvements had taken place since 1895. Included in the scheme was a designated ward for children – a project that would fulfil one of Mr Buston's 'dearest wishes' – and, apart from improved accommodation for the resident staff, new domestic facilities included a scullery, vegetable larder, pantry and storeroom. The laundry was also enlarged and modern appliances purchased including an 'electrically-driven and steam-heated washing machine [and a] hydro-extractor and ironing machine'. Meanwhile, a new, larger mortuary, separate from the Main Block, had been 'a compulsory improvement' to serve the needs of the Infirmary, town and district.[10] With the modernisation of the 'Service Block', which was completed during the summer of 1938, the Infirmary was considered by the Board of Management to be not only 'thoroughly up-to-date' but also 'getting more efficient as the years went by'.[11] These were familiar phrases that had reverberated down the century to those subscribers who chose to listen, as were the 'earnest appeals' for money to liquidate accrued building debts that in 1938 had risen to £2,000 and would not be defrayed until 1942.

In the meantime, with the country on the verge of the Second World War (1939–45), a request came from the Government to use the Infirmary as a 'Casualty Clearing Station' in case of air raids; a request the Board was reluctant to consider until the Government provided them with financial assistance. This came with the introduction of the publically funded Hospital Emergency Scheme (EHS) – later the Emergency Medical Service (EMS) – when, in April 1939, a memorandum from the Ministry of Health selected and classified the Infirmary as 1A for the:

- initial reception of casualties pending transfer and for treatment of cases of immediate urgency among the civilian population;
- general reception and treatment both of casualties and of civilian sick.

Eventually, after many Government directives during 1939 (a period known as the 'phoney war') ten Government stand-by beds were made available in addition to the 55 beds that now existed at the Infirmary. Air Raid Precautions (ARP) were also required to be undertaken, including the erection of 'outside shelters' and 'black-out' to windows, all of which cost the Board 'a great deal' of money.[12]

The Infirmary's trained nurses – whose increased numbers in 1936 comprised a Matron, three sisters and two trained staff nurses supported by two assistant nurses and five probationers – were also required to attend lectures on the treatment of air-raid casualties, and volunteer their services as 'fire-watchers', whilst the Board members were obliged to attend ARP lectures at Quinton, near Birmingham.

For those trained nurses whose salaries and conditions of service were no longer extant, the Board expressed a willingness to contribute, from 1938, to the 'Superannuation Scheme for Nurses'. Incurring an additional expenditure of upwards of £68 per annum, the Board felt it incumbent upon them to participate in a scheme that would provide a nurse with a pension upon retirement, and therefore aid retention! A further development that proved beneficial, both to the Board and the nurses, was the introduction of the 'Rushcliffe Scheme'. Originating in 1941, a committee under the chairmanship of Lord Rushcliffe considered the salaries and working conditions of nurses, assistant nurses and student nurses whose training, since the 1920s, was expected to take place only in approved schools of nursing; a directive seemingly ignored at the Infirmary where 'probationers' were included as members of the nursing staff. The result of the Rushcliffe committee's deliberations, acknowledged by the Government, was an increase in salaries and a comprehensive improvement in working conditions.[13] Implementation was not compulsory but, again, the Infirmary's Board chose to comply with the recommendations as the Government would assist by paying 'about half of the increase in [the nurses'] salaries'.[14] The scheme therefore enabled the Board to obtain and retain sufficient nurses, thus enabling a more efficient service.

During the early 1940s the constant pleas for more subscribers continued, as did the need to raise money, which resulted in increased fees for private patients and maternity cases. The Government also continued to pay for the retention of the ten stand-by beds under the EMS, which Fraser describes as:

> *One of the most significant developments … [as it] … temporarily nationalised all hospital services under a coherent and planned service, in anticipation of mass disruption and injury through bombing. The Emergency Medical Service [also] revealed the diversity of provision and the geographical unevenness of hospital and medical services which were to be an important stimulus in the creation of a National Health Service.*[15]

The incremental and radical development of a national health service was originally conceived in 1938. This development, under formulae evolving from 1939, culminated in the 1946 National Health Service Bill that established the National Health Service in 1948. Of particular relevance was the publication of the Beveridge Report in December 1942, which provided the nation with a foundation for 'the creation of a "comprehensive national health service"'.[16] The 300-page report, which became a best-seller with over 600,000 copies sold,[17] sought to address, through social and economic reforms, the 'five giants' of 'Want, Disease, Ignorance, Squalor and Idleness'. By April 1943 the Infirmary's Board members were suggesting to the subscribers that it was too early to state how the report might affect them as a voluntary hospital. However, in February 1944 the Board had a clearer idea of what the future held when the Coalition Government set out their blueprint for change in a white paper entitled: *A National Health Service*. As in 1911 with the introduction of the National Insurance Act, concerns at the Infirmary existed over the loss of identity, the potential loss of legacies, and hospitals being governed by politicians, whilst the BMA[18] commenced a four-year campaign to oppose a scheme that would be funded through taxation.

With the cessation of hostilities and the withdrawal of the EMS funding in 1945 the Infirmary was, once again, in financial difficulties that would be partially remedied by increasing, yet again, the fees of private and maternity patients.

By April 1947, following record floods, gales, blizzards and drifts of snow 12-feet deep throughout the town and district, there was a general acknowledgment amongst the Board members that change was inevitable. This change was realised by others when, on 5 April 1947, the *Bridgnorth Journal* led with a front page headline that read: 'Nationalisation of the Bridgnorth Infirmary, Major Foster's Remarks at Annual Meeting.' Although there had been a desire to remain a voluntary hospital, the inevitable march of progress in yet another changing world, was accepted with quiet resignation. Uppermost in Major Foster's mind was the desire to hand the Infirmary over to the State, free from debt. To that end, stock in Saving Bonds to the tune of £2,150 was sold to defray current expenses. He also proudly claimed that the Infirmary 'had a capital sum of about £15,500', assets that in July 1948 were expected to be 'in the region of' £7,000.

On Tuesday, 6 April 1948 the Infirmary held their last subscribers' Annual General Meeting at which the resignation of the Honorary Treasurer, Mr W.T. Corfield, was accepted with 'deep gratitude' and the presentation of a gold watch, 'suitably inscribed'. The treasurer's account for the year ending 31 December 1947 identified the Infirmary's total receipts as being £9,587; a sum that was insufficient to meet its needs, as yet further investments and stock were sold to defray expenses. With the general fund account overdrawn and payment of £3,500 for a newly installed X-Ray machine still outstanding, the entire financial situation was summed up by Major Foster when he informed the gathering that:

> It is obvious by the balance sheet we are at the end of our tether as regards running the hospital on our present income. We have done our best but have been beaten by expenses. The new arrangement will certainly save the treasurer a good deal of anxiety as to the future.[19]

Meanwhile, others were duly thanked for their voluntary services that would cease on the 5 July 1948 when the Bridgnorth and South Shropshire Infirmary was nationalised and thus became an integral part of the National Health Service.

It was, in every respect, the end of an era.

Appendix 1

Wording typed upon the reverse of a picture of James Milman Coley:

The back of this picture was repaired in January, 1929. Pasted upon the original back was a lengthy statement written in ink which was somewhat faded; the following is an exact copy of the statement, the original has been placed in the frame at the back of the mount.

NB The above note, including the transcription below, bear the handwritten initials W. W-P, and are considered to be those of Dr Wilfred Watkins-Pitchford, formerly house-surgeon to the Bridgnorth and South Shropshire Infirmary who, in retirement, returned to Bridgnorth where he established himself as a local historian of note.

Presented to Mr. William Coley, by his Aunt Miss Jane Coley, in memory of his Uncle, the late Dr. James Milman Coley, of whom th.. photograph was taken by Mr. Winchester, near London, formerly House Surgeon to the Bridgnorth Infirmary, from an oil painting of Dr. Coley, whilst at Brussels, about 1848, at a cost of £200, and sent for sale to the London Exhibition of 1851; but not finding there a purchaser, the said Mr. Winchester advanced a sum of money upon it for Dr. Coley, at whose death in 1867 Mr. Winchester kindly presented the oil picture to his son, Revd. James Coley, Vicar of Cowley, Oxfordshire, in whose possession it now remains. Doctor James Milman Coley was born August 30, 1784 and died 1867, November 12 at South Lambeth, aged 83. He was formerly Surgeon of Bridgnorth, and afterwards Physician to the British Embassy, at Brussels.

Bridgnorth, St. John Street,
December 24, 1870

Notes:

1. A certified copy of an entry of death for James Milman Coley gives the date of his death as the 'Eleventh November 1867', not 12 November 1867.

2. Jane Coley, born 7 May 1796, at Bridgnorth, was the sister of James Milman Coley and the youngest of all the children born to William and Elizabeth Coley. The 1871 census shows Jane, a spinster, residing at No. 8 St John Street, Bridgnorth where she was the head of the household and described as a 'Fund Holder'. Residing with her was her servant, Sarah Sherry.

3. All items submitted to the Great Exhibition of 1851 were judged and recorded in the 'Reports of the Juries'. As Class xxx (Fine Arts) did not include paintings (other than those on either ceramics, textiles or glass), Jane Coley's assertion that Dr Coley attempted to sell his portrait (in oils) to the 'London Exhibition of 1851' is open to question.

Appendix 2

Bridgnorth and South Shropshire Infirmary.
PRIVATE NURSES' DEPARTMENT.
REGULATIONS FOR PRIVATE NURSES.

APPLICATIONS	1.	All applications should be made to the Matron.
CHARGES	2.	The charge for the services of a Nurse shall be as follows:

Medical or Surgical Cases - £1 5s. a week or part of a week.
     ,,   ,,   - £1 1s. a week after the first week.
Typhoid   - - -   - £1 10s. a week or part of a week.
Attendance at an Operation - 10/6
Attendance for One Day   - 10/6
Attendance for One Night - 10/6
When for the convenience of patients, nurses return to sleep at the Infirmary, an extra charge of one shilling and sixpence a day is made.

TRAVELLING AND LAUNDRY EXPENSES	3.	All travelling and laundry expenses are to be paid by the family employing the Nurse.
LIMIT OF ATTENDANCE	4.	No Nurse will be permitted to remain with the same Patient for more than one month, without special leave from the Matron.
TRANSFERS	5.	No Nurse may be passed on from one family to another.
WITHDRAWAL	6.	The Matron has power to withdraw Nurses at any time with the consent of the medical man in charge of the case.
GRATUITIES	7.	Nurses are not allowed to receive any gifts in money.
DUTIES OF NURSE	8.	The Nurse shall take the whole charge of the Patient when on duty, and shall superintend the cleaning, etc., of the sick room.
RELAXATION OF NURSE	9.	The Nurse must be allowed reasonable time for rest in every twenty-four hours, and two hours daily out of doors for exercise. When her services are required at night, she must be allowed seven consecutive hours of rest out of the sick room, and at least one hour out of doors daily for exercise in the day time.
UNIFORM	10.	The nurse shall wear her uniform at all times.
MEALS	11.	The Nurse's meals may not be taken in the sick room, and not with the servants of the house. When on night service, extra tea, coffee or cocoa shall be provided for her.
STIMULANTS	12.	No wine or spirits may be given to the Nurse.

Source: Bridgnorth Hospital Records, Bridgnorth Infirmary, Reports 1896–1920, for the year 1901, 18–19.

Appendix 3

Hymn No. 368, 'Thou to whom the sick and dying'

This hymn, from *The Victorian Ancient and Modern (A&M) English Hymnal*, was sung by the joint choirs of St Leonard and St Mary Magdalene churches, Bridgnorth, at the laying of the foundation stone of the Bridgnorth and South Shropshire Infirmary on 24 April 1895 and again on 6 December 1928 at the opening of the Infirmary's new wings. *The Victorian Hymnal*, with its often sentimental wording, was revised in 1906 by The Revd Percy Dearmer (1867–1936) and the composer Ralph Vaughan Williams (1872–1958), since when several further editions have appeared.

> Thou to Whom the sick and dying
> Ever came, nor came in vain,
> Still with healing word replying
> To the wearied cry of pain,
> Hear us, Jesu, as we meet
> Suppliants at Thy mercy – seat.
>
> Still the weary, sick, and dying
> Need a brother's, sister's care,
> On Thy higher help relying
> May we now their burden share,
> Bringing all our offerings meet
> Suppliants at Thy mercy – seat.
>
> May each child of Thine be willing,
> Willing both in hand and heart,
> All the law of love fulfilling,
> Ever comfort to impart,
> Ever bringing offerings meet
> Suppliant to Thy mercy – seat.
>
> So may sickness, sin and sadness
> To Thy healing virtue yield,
> Till the sick and sad, in gladness,
> Rescued, ransom'd, cleansed, heal'd,
> One in Thee together meet,
> Pardon'd at Thy judgement seat.

Appendix 4

The Imperial Monetary System

Prior to the introduction of the metric monetary system in February 1971 when the pound was decimalised as 100 (new) pence ('p'), Britain's monetary system was based on the Imperial (Roman) system of pounds ('L' or '£'), shillings ('s') and pence ('d') when the pound was represented by 240 pence. The abbreviated forms are derived from Latin, hence the pound or 'L' comes from libra (a pound weight), whilst the sign '£' represents the letter 'L' of libra; the shilling or 's' comes from solidus (a Roman gold coin) and the penny/ pence (plural) or 'd' comes from denarius (a Roman silver coin).

Coin	Denomination	Common Parlance
Half-farthing	⅛ of a penny (d)	
Farthing	¼ of a penny (¼d)	farthin'
Halfpenny	½ a penny (½d)	Ha'p'ny
Penny	one penny (1d)	'copper'
Twopence	(2d)	tuppence or tup'ny bit
Threepence	(3d)	thrupence or thrup'ny bit or 'alf-a-tanner
Groat (silver)	four pence (4d)	'Joey' (1836–1855)
Sixpence	(6d)	'tanner'
Shilling	one shilling, 1s or 1/- (12d to the shilling)	'bob'
Florin	two shillings, 2s or 2/- (24 pence)	two-bob piece
Half-Crown	two shillings & 6 pence, or 2/6 (30 pence)	two 'n six or 'alf-a-crown
Crown	five shillings, 5s or 5/- (60 pence)	Five bob
Half-Sovereign	ten shilling coin, 10s or 10/- then as a banknote (120 pence)	ten bob, especially as a banknote
Sovereign	one pound coin then £1 note (20s or 240d)	As a banknote : a 'quid'
Guinea	one pound, one shilling; 1g or 1gn	'ginee'

Banknotes, originally produced in various denominations by local banks for local use (including those in Bridgnorth) were replaced from the mid-nineteenth century onwards by Bank of England notes for use in England and Wales, whilst Scotland always produced its own notes. Initially issued by the treasury in sums of £5 and over, banknotes were introduced in 1914 for one pound and for ten shillings.

When written, monetary values were variously expressed, for example, as: £3 4s 2d (pronounced 'three pounds four and tuppence'); 2s 6d or 2/6 (pronounced 'two and six'); 3½d (pronounced 'thruppence ha'p'ny'). One Guinea, minted originally from the gold of that West African country, represented one pound, one shilling and was written as 1g. or 1gn.

Appendix 5

Imperial Linear Measurements

A rood, also known as a rod, pole or perch, was a superficial measurement of land in which the perch (a rod or pole of a definite length) consisted of 5.5 yards. However, variations occurred locally from 5.5 yards to 8 yards.

On 13 February 1835 Mr Whitmore's agent, Mr Branson, confirmed the land measurements of the prospective Bridgnorth Infirmary in New Town as being 'about one rood, six perches statute measure'; a local measurement that may have conformed to 5.5 yards but one which cannot be verified.

The basic unit of measurement was the yard.

Imperial			Metric
1 yard	= 3 feet	= 36 inches	0.91 m
5.5 yards	= 1 rod		
22 yards	= 1 chain	= 4 rods	
220 yards	= 1 furlong	= 10 chains	
1760 yards	= 1 mile	= 8 furlongs	1.61 km

For an historical overview of 'The Division and Measurement of Land in England' by Barry Moss, see the *Building Engineer*, May 1995, 19–21.

Notes and References

Abbreviations

BHR = Bridgnorth Hospital Records. Various documents including Annual General Meeting Reports for the Bridgnorth Dispensary and the Bridgnorth Infirmary.

SA = Shropshire Archives.

SA 2740/1: Bridgnorth Infirmary, General Meetings 1832–1841.
SA 2740/2: Bridgnorth Infirmary, General Meetings 1841–1870.
SA 2740/3: Bridgnorth Infirmary, Trustees, 4 November 1835 – 3 January 1871.
SA 2740/4: ditto, Committee Meetings, 1 December 1832 – 23 October 1840.
SA 2740/5: ditto, Committee Meetings, 6 April 1841 – 6 March 1851.
SA 2740/6: ditto, Monthly Committee Meetings, 3 April 1851 – 30 March 1866.
SA 2740/7: ditto, Monthly Committee Meetings, 5 April 1866 – 2 December 1870.
SA 2740/8: ditto, Treasurer, 1836–1870.
SA 2740/9: ditto, Treasurer, 1841.
SA 2740/10: Bridgnorth Infirmary and Dispensary, 1871.
SA 2740/11: ditto, Doctor's Visiting Book, March 1885–August 1895.
SA 2740/12: Bridgnorth and South Shropshire Infirmary, Doctor's Visiting Book, August 1895–May 1902.

TBDHS = Trustees Bridgnorth and District Historical Society. Guardians of the Northgate Museum, its artefacts and documents.

1 Conflicts of Interest

1.	*Wolverhampton Chronicle*, Wednesday 5 December 1832, Vol. xxii, No. 1148, Wolverhampton Archives and Local Studies Centre.
2.	*Shrewsbury Chronicle*, Friday 9 October 1835, No. 3292. SA: Reel 116, 1834–1836
3.	*Salopian Journal*, Monday 12 October 1835 in *Watton's Cuttings*, 3, 64–6. SA.
4.	Loudon, I.S.L., 'The Origins and Growth of the Dispensary Movement in England', *Bulletin of the History of Medicine*, Vol. 55 (1981), 322–42 (323).
5.	Science Museum, London: Medical History, Gallery 4, Cabinet I, 36, 'Therapy'.
6.	Cherry, Steven, *Medical services and the hospitals in Britain, 1860–1939* (Cambridge University Press, 1996), 43.

7. TBDHS, ref. 2669: Notification of a General Meeting, 10 November 1832, to the subscribers of the Bridgnorth Dispensary concerning new rules.

8. Loudon, I.S.L., 'The Origins and Growth of the Dispensary Movement in England', *Bulletin of the History of Medicine*, Vol. 55, (1981), 324–5. Table 1: 'Voluntary Hospitals and Dispensaries Established in England during the 18th Century'.

9. BHR: Folder No. 1. Bridgnorth Dispensary Annual Reports, 24 December 1835.

10. SA/4001/P/1/8: A map of Bridgnorth town by John Wood, 1835.

11. Flinn, M.W., 'Medical Services under the New Poor Law', in Fraser, Derek (ed.), *The New Poor Law in the Nineteenth Century* (Macmillan, 1976), 45.

12. BHR: Folder No. 4. A printed notice 'To the Inhabitants of Bridgnorth and the Neighbourhood' with handwritten amendments, dated 11 March 1835, that is adhered to a piece of wood.

13. Bynum, W.F., *Science and the Practice of Medicine in the Nineteenth Century* (Cambridge University Press, 1996), 5–6.

14. Donnison, Jean, *Midwives and Medical Men: A History of the Struggle for the Control of Childbirth* (Historical Publications, 1999), 55. See also NOTES, Ch3, 14 at 216.

15. Holloway, S.W.F., 'Medical Education in England, 1830–1858: A Sociological Analysis', *History*, XLIX, (1964), 299–324, (312).

16. SA: DA2/112/1, Committee of Health Minute Book, 7 September 1849.

17. Wanklyn, Malcolm: personal communication.

18. SA/0/21: Rogers, William, 'Report to the General Board of Health on Bridgnorth', (1853), 14, 'Personal inspection of the District'.

19. BHR: Folder No. 3. Bridgnorth Dispensary (Notices).

20. Summers, Anne, *Angels and Citizens: British Women as Military Nurses 1854–1914* (Threshold Press, 2000), 7.

21. Bynum, W.F., *Science and the Practice of Medicine in the Nineteenth Century* (Cambridge University Press, 1996), 75.

22. Cartwright, Frederick, F., *The Development of Modern Surgery* (Arthur Baker, 1967), 3–10.

23. *Wolverhampton Chronicle*, Wednesday 5 December 1832, Vol. xxxii, No. 1148. Wolverhampton Archives and Local Studies Centre.

24. SA: 3214/1, Report on the Borough of Bridgnorth laid before Parliament since 1831, 205–6.

25. SA: Class q C55.7, Accn. No. 5189/1 Salop 1832, Register of Voters (Southern Division).

26. Wanklyn, Malcolm, 'Urban revival in early modern England: Bridgnorth and the river trade, 1660–1800', *Midland History*, (1993), 18, 37–64, (59), including personal communication.

27. Fussell, G.E., 'Four Centuries of Farming Systems in Shropshire 1500–1900', *Transactions Shropshire Archaeological Society* (hereafter TSAS), liv, 1–29, (18).
28. SA: 2740/4, 23 December 1835, Committee Meeting.
29. Ibid. 1835.
30. Ibid. 1835.
31. SA: 2740/1, Notice of Resolutions passed at a Public Meeting held in the Town Hall on Thursday 29 November 1832 and the necessity to establish an Infirmary. (Loose sheet).

2 A GOAL ACHIEVED

1. SA: 2740/4. Much in this section is derived from these records.
2. TBDHS, ref. 2529: 13 July 1833.
3. Stevenson, Christine, *Medicine and Magnificence: British Hospital and Asylum Architecture 1660–1815* (Yale University Press, 2000), 153.
4. SA: 2740/4, 7 November 1834.
5. Head, F.W., *Weaving in Bridgnorth*, (1947), 64. Printer J. Teece, Bridgnorth. TBDHS, ref. 2001/55.
6. SA: 2740/4, 14 February 1835.
7. McMenemey, W.H., *A History of the Worcestershire Royal Infirmary* (Press Alliances, 1947).
8. SA: *Watton's Cuttings*, 3, 64–6.
9. *Shrewsbury Chronicle*, Friday 9 October 1835, No. 3292. SA: Reel 116, 1834–1836.
10. SA: *Watton's Cuttings*, 3, 64–6.
11. Flinn, M.W., 'Medical Services under the New Poor Law', in Fraser, Derek, (ed.), *The New Poor Law in the Nineteenth Century* (Macmillan, 1976), 46–7.
12. Richardson, Harriet, (ed.), *English Hospitals 1660–1948: A Survey of their Architecture and Design*, Ch. 3 Cottage Hospitals, 47. (Royal Commission on the Historical Monuments of England, hereafter RCHME, 1998). The gazetteer of sites records the Bridgnorth and South Shropshire Infirmary, that is now known as the Bridgnorth Hospital.
13. SA: 2740/10
14. Chang, Jack H.T., MD., Bibliography of James Milman Coley, Table 1, 17–18, in *James Milman Coley: A Practical Treatise on the Diseases of Children, Pediatric* [sic] *Surgery*, London, 1846. A paper presented to the British Association of Paediatric Surgeons, Glasgow (1990).
15. SA: *Watton's Cuttings*, 3, 64–6.
16. SA: 2740/8.

17. SA: 2740/4, 30 November 1835.

18. *Wolverhampton Chronicle*, 10 August 1836, Vol. xxvi, No. 1340. Wolverhampton Archives and Local Studies Centre. The Infirmary had been open six months when the Trustees met on 3 August 1836. It is therefore assumed that the Infirmary opened on the 3 February 1836.

19. *The Bridgnorth Almanack*, Chronological Table of Local Events, (1905), 52. Bridgnorth Library, Local Studies Section.

20. Jarvis, G.A; Hubbard, K; Billingsley, D., *Bridgnorth and its Water Conduits* (July 1996), a report presented to the members of the Bridgnorth Civic Society that identifies four different types of water conduits and their locations in the town.

21. BHR: Folder No. 2. The Second Annual Report of the Bridgnorth Infirmary, 1837, Expenditure, 2.

22. *Wolverhampton Chronicle*, 10 August 1836, Vol. xxvi, No. 1340. Wolverhampton Archives and Local Studies Centre.

23. Newby, Howard, *Country Life: A Social History of Rural England* (Weidenfeld and Nicolson, 1987), 73.

24. Bynum, W.F., *Science and the Practice of Medicine in the Nineteenth Century* (Cambridge University Press, 1996), 85.

25. SA: 2740/3, 21 September 1837.

26. BHR: Folder No. 1. Bridgnorth Dispensary Annual reports for 1835 and 1840.

27. BHR: Folder No. 2. Bridgnorth Infirmary, Second Annual Report for 1837.

3 DISSENSION AT THE INFIRMARY

1. TBDHS, ref 439. The Coley family's *Book of Common Prayer and Administration of the Sacraments*, (University of Cambridge, 1637), with an incomplete family record.

2. James, R.R., FRCS, 'Medical Men in Practice in Shropshire, 1779–1783' in TSAS, Series 4, Vol. 7, Bridgnorth, 215.

3. TBDHS, ref 439. The Coley family's *Book of Common Prayer and Administration of the Sacraments*, (University of Cambridge, 1637).

4. James, R.R., FRCS, 'Medical Men in Practice in Shropshire, 1779–1783' in TSAS, Series 4, Vol. 7, Bridgnorth, 215.

5. Guildhall Library, London: Ms 8241/6, relating to John Coley (Junior), LSA. John Coley, Junior, baptised 30 December 1811, was apprenticed to his grandfather, William Coley, on 7 November 1826 for seven years and gained his licentiateship on 24 October 1833 having attended the London Hospital for 12 months.

6. Bridgnorth Burgess Book: Bridgnorth Library, Local Studies. The Coley's are listed thus:
    Coley, William, Surgeon, Bridgnorth, 18 February 1789.
    Coley, John, Veterinary Surgeon, Bridgnorth, Son of William, 29 Sept. 1805.
    Coley, James Milman, Surgeon, Bridgnorth, Another son of William, 18 Aug. 1807.
    Coley, John, Surgeon, Bridgnorth, Son of John, 20 July 1835.

7. Cartwright, Frederick, F., *The Development of Modern Surgery from 1830* (Arthur Barker, 1967), 9.

8. Chang, Jack H.T., M.D., *James Milman Coley: A Practical Treatise on the Diseases of Children, Pediatric* [sic] *Surgery*, London, 1846. Introduction to the paper, (1990), 1. ('History of British Pediatric [sic] Surgery Coley').

9. Porter, Roy, *The Greatest Benefit to Mankind: A Medical History of Humanity from Antiquity to the Present* (Fontana, 1999), 361.

10. *The Law Advertiser*, 1830, Vol. viii, 366: Partnership Dissolved, 1 July 1830.

11. Harvie, Christopher, 'Revolution and the Rule of Law (1789–1851)', in Morgan, Kenneth O., (ed.), *The Oxford Popular History of Britain* (Oxford University Press, 1993), 495–7; see also Whigs (British Political Party) at: http://en.wikipedia.org/wiki/Whigs_(British_political_party) for an historical overview from 1678–1868 and transition to Liberal Party. Accessed 3/6/15.

12. Mason, J.F.A., 'Parliamentary Representation, 1832–1885, Bridgnorth', in *Victoria County History of Shropshire* (hereafter VCH), Vol. iii (1979), 331.

13. *Shrewsbury Chronicle*, 13 October 1837, Bridgnorth. NB Coley is spelt 'Colley'.

14. Mason, J.F.A., 'Bridgnorth Town Clerks 1525–1974', in *VCH*, Vol. lxxiv (1999), 29–31. Mason remarks that the introduction of the 1835 Municipal Corporation Act 'made little difference to the office [of town clerk].'

15. Municipal Corporations Act at: http://en.wikipedia.org/wiki/Municipal_Corporations_Act_1835 for an overview of the legislation that lists Bridgnorth as one of 178 reformed boroughs. Accessed 3/6/15.

16. Elliott, Douglas J., *Policing in Shropshire 1836–1967* (K.F.A. Brewin, 1984), The Borough of Bridgnorth, 6.

17. *Bridgnorth Journal*, Correspondence, 8 August & 15 August 1903, 5. Bridgnorth Library. Local Studies.

18. *Ten Towns Messenger*, Friday, 11 August 1837, Vol. ii, No. 57. Kidderminster Reference Library. See also VCH, Vol. iii, (1979) 332.

19. Weyman, Henry T., 'The Members of Parliament for Bridgnorth, No. 171, Henry Hanbury Tracy, (Whig), 1837', in *Transactions of the Shropshire Archaeological and Historical Society* (hereafter TSAHS), 4th Series, Vol. v, 72, 1915; Randall, J.,

The Tourist's Guide to Bridgnorth, (Evans, Edkins and McMichael, 1875), 46, for year 1837. A facsimile from the original published by Salop County Library, undated.

20.   *Bridgnorth Journal*, Correspondence, 1 August 1903, 5.

21.   SA: 2740/4, 3 August 1837.

22.   The Royal College of Surgeons of Edinburgh, Library Service with thanks to a member of staff for a full explanation of 'Diploma' which is condensed below. The 'Diploma', originally introduced in 1757 at the request of the War Office, was fully introduced and developed in the 1770s to provide surgeons with a recognised qualification. From 1815 onwards the 'Diploma' was standardised and renamed 'Licentiateship'. However, the term 'Diploma' continued to be used, as exemplified by James Henry Martin during the 1830s.

23.   Chang, Jack H.T., MD, *James Milman Coley: A Practical Treatise …*, a paper presented to the British Association of Paediatric Surgeons, (1990), Table 1, 17.

24.   Porter, Roy, *The Greatest Benefit to Mankind* (Fontana, 1999), 354; Porter, Roy, *Disease, medicine and society in England, 1550–1860* (Cambridge University Press, 1993), 45–6.

25.   *The Salopian Journal*, Wednesday 20 June 1838 in *Watton's Cuttings*, Vol. 1, 381–4. SA.

26.   *Shrewsbury Chronicle*, 13 October 1837, Bridgnorth; *Ten Towns Messenger*, 26 October 1838, Bridgnorth Conservative Association.

27.   Coley, J.M., *A Faithful Report of the Late Disgraceful Proceedings at the Bridgnorth Infirmary* (hereafter *A Faithful Report*), (Joseph Bridgen, 1839), 45. Cushing/ Whitney Medical Historical Library, University of Yale, USA.

28.   SA: 2740/4, 14 June 1838. See also: 21 June and 3 July 1838.

29.   *VCH*, Vol. ii, 143 (1973), (2) Bridgnorth Grammar School.

30.   Coley, J.M., (1839) *A Faithful Report*, 40.

31.   *The London Gazette*, 2 November 1838, Issue 19669, 2385.

32.   Bridgnorth Medical Practice, North Gate House, 7 High Street, Bridgnorth. In the Boardroom of North Gate House, previously the home of Dr William Rhodes and then Dr L.E. Dickson, a photograph of an oil painting of James Milman Coley is displayed. Upon the back is a typed note stating that the picture was repaired in January 1929. The author of the note, initialled W. W-P, is considered to be Dr Wilfred Watkins-Pitchford who, in retirement, returned to Bridgnorth in 1926. See Appendix 1 for the note's contents. NB Bridgnorth Medical Practice relocated to a purpose-built primary health care centre in the grounds of Bridgnorth Hospital (previously the Bridgnorth and South Shropshire Infirmary) on 8 May 2007.

33.   Coley, J.M., (1839) *A Faithful Report*, 7.

34. *Ten Towns Messenger*, Friday 7 December 1838, Vol. III, No. 126. Kidderminster Reference Library.

35. Holloway, S.W.F., 'Medical Education in England, 1830–1858: A Sociological Analysis', in *History*, XLIX, (1964), 299–324 (see 308–10).

36. Wilson, A., 'Conflict, Consensus and Charity: Politics and Provincial Voluntary Hospitals in the Eighteenth Century', in *English Historical Review*, Vol. iii, (1996), 599–619; Elliott, Paul, 'Medical Institutions, Scientific Culture and Urban Improvements in Late-Georgian England: The Politics of the Derbyshire General Infirmary', in Reinarz, Jonathan, (ed.), *Medicine and Society in the Midlands 1750–1950*, Midland History Occasional Paper, (2007), 27–46.

37. SA: Classmark 055.7, vf Ref. No. XLS 1504, Bridgnorth Poll Book (1837).

38. Fraser, Antonia, *Perilous Question: Reform or Revolution? Britain on the Brink, 1832* (Public Affairs, 2013), 141.

39. SA: 2740/4, 4 March 1839; Coley, J.M., (1839), *A Faithful Report*, 11.

40. The Worshipful Society of Apothecaries of London, Archives: The Apothecaries' Hall Record Book for 26 September 1839 and 3 October 1839; *London Medical Gazette*, Vol. 25, 112, List of Gentlemen who have received Certificates, Thursday 3 October 1839, James Henry Martin, Bridgnorth, Salop.

41. Coley, J.M. (1839) *A Faithful Report*, 6.

42. SA: 2740/4, 21 June 1838.

43. Coley, J.M. (1839), *A Faithful Report*, 12–13.

44. SA: 2740/4, 5 April 1839; Coley, J.M., (1839) *A Faithful Report*, 20.

45. SA: 2740/3, 22 June 1839.

46. SA: 2740/3, 1 August 1839; Coley, J.M., (1839) *A Faithful Report*, 22–23.

47. Coley, J.M., (1839), *A Faithful Report*, 26; SA: 2740/4, 21 August 1839.

48. Coley, J.M.,(1839), *A Faithful Report*, 28–29.

49. *Shrewsbury Chronicle*, Friday 18 October 1839, 2.

50. SA: 2740/4, 16 October 1839.

51. SA /DA2/296/1: Bridgnorth Infirmary, Public Notice. Copy of Mrs Griffiths' Letter to the [Infirmary] Committee headed Brierly Hill, 13 January 1840. See Coley (1839), *A Faithful Report*, 33 for the full 'Deposition of Mrs Griffiths'.

52. SA: 2740/4, 28 February 1840.

53. SA: 2740/3, 23 October 1839.

54. *Hereford Journal*, 28 October 1840, Bridgnorth Quarter Sessions.

55. SA/2740/1: 5 November 1840.

56. *VCH*, Vol. ii, 142–3, (1973), (2) Bridgnorth Grammar School.

57. SA/DA2/134/2/21: Grand Jury Room, Bridgnorth, 24 October 1842. Report of the Committee of Magistrates, appointed by the Town Council 30 September 1842. Chairman, J.M. Coley. Others present: J. Smalman, Henry Slater Richards, Thomas Bangham and Joshua Sing.

58. Medical Directory 1845, Bridgenorth [*sic*]. See also *James Milman Coley – notes on his movements* by Geoffrey Davenport (former Librarian), Royal College of Physicians, London.

59. SA/4752/2/54: 'Valuation of Premises and Fixtures of Dr Coley' by T. Nock of Bridgnorth, which itemises various rooms and outbuildings; SRO/4752/3/58: 'Property Sale Book 1847' with the date of the sale.

60. SA/2740/2

61. Anon, *Bridgnorth Hospital*, Bridgnorth Library, Local Studies. It has been suggested that these anonymous and undated four pages of A4 may have been written by Dr 'Agie' Campbell who, as Consort of the Mayor, Councillor, Miss Jean Algie formed, with others, the Bridgnorth Hospital Action Group in July 1983. This followed the Shropshire Health Authority's intention to downgrade the Bridgnorth and South Shropshire Infirmary to a geriatric hospital; a proposition that did not succeed. Within the anonymous text is a reference to the indenture of 25 March 1841 that existed within the Bridgnorth Hospital Records until the 1990s. Attempts to trace the document have failed.

62. *Bagshaw's Shropshire Directory 1851*, 619. See also 617 and listing of James Henry Martin as one of 12 Town Councillors.

63. Martin Family Tree at: http://users.iconz.co.nz/kimo/family_tree/d0001/g0000060.htm (accessed 8/5/15); Chadwick, Gwynne, *Bridgnorth - News and Events between 1852–1900* (Privately published, 2006). See 28 November, 20 and 7 September, 65 for notices of death that would have taken about two months to arrive in England from New Zealand; see also *Bridgnorth Journal* (m/f) Bridgnorth Library, Local Studies.

64. Certified Copy of an entry of death for James Milman Coley.

65. *Ten Towns Messenger*, Friday 26 October 1838, 'Bridgnorth Conservative Association'. Kidderminster Reference Library.

66. Mason, J.F.A., *The Borough of Bridgnorth 1157–1957*, Ch. 5, The Whitmores and Bridgnorth, (Bridgnorth Borough Council, 1957), 30–34. Bridgnorth Library, Local Studies, S9/901.

1. Ives, A.G.L., *British Hospitals* (Collins, 1948), 14–15.
2. *Wolverhampton Chronicle*, Wednesday 5 December 1832, Vol. xxii, No. 1148. Wolverhampton Archives and Local Studies Centre.
3. Stevenson, Christine, *Medicine and Magnificence British Hospitals and Asylum Architecture 1660–1815* (Yale University Press, 2000), 3.
4. *Wolverhampton Chronicle*, Wednesday 5 December 1832, Vol. xxii, No. 1148.
5. SA 2740/10: Bridgnorth Infirmary and Dispensary 1871 which holds the 'Report and Balance Sheet' for 1885. Much in this section is derived from these records.
6. BHR, Folder No. 6: *Speech of the Bishop of Hereford at the Annual Meeting of the Bridgnorth and South Shropshire Infirmary at the Town Hall, Bridgnorth, on Friday, January 31st, 1890*. Reprinted as a public poster and an A4 sheet.
7. SA 4752/59/101: Nock Deighton Valuation Book 1896–1897, Folio No. 1, 1. Value of Fixtures and Fittings at the Old Infirmary, 1896, £20 4s.
8. Hawker, Jean, *A Short History of Bridgnorth's Hospitals* (Bridgnorth Publications and Design, 1996), 3. Miss Hawker, SRN, was first Matron and then Hospital Manager of the Bridgnorth Hospital, 1974–89.
9. SA 4752/59/101: Nock Deighton Valuation Book 1896–1897, Folio No. 1, 1.
10. SA 2740/8
11. BHR: Folder No. 6, *Speech of the Bishop of Hereford*, 31 January 1890.
12. BHR: Folder No. 2, The Second Annual Report of the Bridgnorth Infirmary 1842.
13. Wanklyn, M.D.G., (ed.), *The Diary of George Gitton of Bridgnorth for 1866*, Centre for Local History, University of Keele, (1998). Shropshire Record Series, Volume 2.
14. Oddy, D.J., 'Food, drink, nutrition', in Thompson, F.M.L., (ed.) *The Cambridge Social History of Britain 1750–1950*, Vol. 2, 'People and their Environment' (Cambridge University Press, 1990), 264.
15. Randall, J., *The Tourist's Guide to Bridgnorth*, (Evans, Edkins, McMichael, 1875), 59, Water Supply. Reproduced in facsimile by Salop County Library (undated); Grose, Valerie, *A Short History of the Water Supply of Bridgnorth*, (undated) leaflet in which Grose states that: 'in 1851, the waterworks were only capable of supplying about 180 houses out of 1,200 in the town with Severn water'.
16. Eveleigh, David, J., *Bogs, Baths and Basins: The Story of Domestic Sanitation* (Sutton, 2002), 15; The Public Health Act (1848): the Act, the first of its kind, established a national General Board of Health and the provision of local boards of health where the death rate exceeded 23 per 1,000. Following the 1853 Sanitary Report, the Bridgnorth Local Board of Health undertook work that included: improving the water supply, laying main drains and closing cave dwellings. House

numbering and the creation of a cemetery, outside the town, also commenced in the 1850s.

17. Rogers, William, Report to the General Board of Health on Bridgnorth, (1853), 14. SA 0/21.

18. *Bridgnorth Journal*, 26 May 1855 and 8 March 1856.

19. BHR Folder 5: Circular *'Tis Sixty Years Since'*, (Bemrose & Sons, December 1893). An appeal by the Committee of the Bridgnorth and South Shropshire Infirmary for a further £1,000 towards the estimated cost of £4,000 for the new building.

20. Dickens, Charles, *Martin Chuzzlewitt*, (1883–4), Preface, Chapters XIX, XXV. (Chancellor Press, 1994).

21. Summers, Anne, 'The Mysterious Demise of Sarah Gamp: The Domiciliary Nurse and Her Detractors, *c.*1830–1860', in *Victorian Studies*, Spring, Vol. 32, (1989), 365–86.

22. Ibid. 365.

23. Quoted in Abel-Smith, Brian, *A History of the Nursing Profession* (Heinemann, 1960), 5-6. Note 1, *Hospital*, 6 June 1914, 276, 6.

24. Howie, William Bruce, 'Complaints and Complaint Procedures in the Eighteenth- and early Nineteenth-century Provincial Hospitals in England', in *Medical History*, 25 (1981), 345–62. SA 5764/7/2.

25. BHR, Folder 2: Bridgnorth Infirmary, Thirteenth Annual Report, 1853, income.

26. Eveleigh, David, J., *Bogs, Baths, and Basins: The Story of Domestic Sanitation* (Sutton, 2002), 64–5.

27. *Ten Towns Messenger*, Friday 18 June 1841, (2nd ed.), No. CCXLX. Kidderminster Reference Library.

28. Oddy, D.J., 'Food, drink, and nutrition', in Thompson, F.M.L. (ed.), *The Cambridge Social History of Britain 1750–1950*, Vol. 2, 'People and Their Environment' (Cambridge University Press, 1990), 252–3.

29. Howie, William Bruce, 'Complaints and Complaint Procedures in the Eighteenth- and early Nineteenth-century Provincial Hospitals in England', in *Medical History*, 25 (1981), 345–62. SA 5764/7/2.

30. Rogers, William, Report to the General Board of Health on Bridgnorth, (1853), 13–14. SA 0 21.

31. Oddy, D.J., 'Food, drink and nutrition', in Thompson, F.M.L., (ed.), *The Cambridge Social History of Britain 1750–1950*, Vol. 2, 'People and their Environment', (Cambridge University Press, 1990), 274.

32. Wildman, Stuart, 'Changes in Hospital Nursing in the West Midlands, 1841–1901', in *Medicine and Society in the Midlands 1750–1950*, Reinarz, Jonathan, (ed.), (Midland History Occasional Publications, 2007), 102–4.

33. SA 2746/6.

34. Woodham-Smith, Cecil, *Florence Nightingale 1820–1910* (Collins Fontana, 1964), 265–9.

35. Wanklyn, M.D.G., (ed.), *The Diary of George Gitton of Bridgnorth for 1866*, Centre for Local History, University of Keele, (1998), 13 & 14 November and 5 December. Shropshire Record Series, Volume 2.

36. *Shrewsbury Chronicle*, 16 November 1866.

37. SA, Accession No. 5424/1/1-54, (unpublished) Diaries of George Gitton, Bridgnorth, 1883–4, which are incomplete and unbound. I am indebted to Prof. M. Wanklyn for introducing me to this document and for his willingness to discuss my transcription of George Gitton's small and difficult hand.

38. SA 2740/2.

39. SA 2740/3.

40. BHR, Folder 2: AGM Report 1871.

41. London Metropolitan Archives, St John's House Records: HO1/ST/SJ/C/04/001: Probationers' Register 1850–1900; HO1/ST/SJ/C/02/001 – Nurses' Register 1850–1865. Personal communication.

42. London Metropolitan Archives, Information Leaflet No. 9, History of Nursing, Major Sources, St John's House (H1/ST/SJ), 8 at: http://www.cityofLondon.gov.uk. (Accessed January 2006).

43. Quoted in Bonham-Carter, Victor, (ed.), *Surgeon in the Crimea, the experiences of George Lawson recorded in letters to his family 1854–1855* (History Book Club, 1968), 5. Note 5, Records of St John's House, 183.

44. SA 2740/10.

45. *Bridgnorth Journal*, 7 February 1891, 5.

5 CHANGE AND CONTINUITY

1. *Bridgnorth Journal*, 27 April 1895, 5.

2. *Bridgnorth Journal*, 15 September 1894, 8. 'Death under Chloroform' at Kidderminster Infirmary. About 3 drachms administered on a piece of lint.

3. Waller, John, *The Discovery of the Germ* (Icon, 2004), Chapter 9.

4. Ibid. Chapter 12.

5. Porter, Roy, *The Greatest Benefit to Mankind a Medical History of Humanity from Antiquity to the Present* (Fontana, 1999), 375.

6. Quoted in Helmstadter, Carol, 'Early Nursing Reform in Nineteenth-Century London: A Doctor Driven Phenomenon', *Medical History*, 46 (2002), 325–50, 349 at: http://www.pubmedcentral.gov/voluntaryhospitals. This site is no longer

available, but a PDF file of the complete article can now (2018) be found at: https://www.ncbi.nlm.nih.gov/pmc/articles/PMC1044527. The paper focuses on the Westminster Hospital and the gradual development of the new nursing from the end of the Napoleonic Wars until 1880, a date generally given for the birth of the modern trained nurse (327).

7. Richardson, Harriet, (ed.), *English Hospitals 1660–1948, A Survey of their Architecture and Design* (RCHME, 1998), 34.

8. *Bridgnorth Journal*, 7 February 1891, 5.

9. SA 2740/10: Report of the House Committee, 1885.

10. BHR, Folder No. 2: Bridgnorth Infirmary and Dispensary, Report of the Committee for 1883.

11. Derbyshire Record Office, personal communication.

12. Helmstadter, Carol, 'Early Nursing Reform in Nineteenth-Century London: A Doctor Driven Phenomenon', *Medical History*, 46, (2002), 326.

13. SA 2740/10: Report of the House Committee, 1885, Work of the Institution, Matron's Work.

14. Ibid. 1885, Matron's Work.

15. Ibid. 1885, Ward 2 opening.

16. *Bridgnorth Journal*, 28 January 1888, 5.

17. *Bridgnorth Journal*, 19 January 1889, 5.

18. Lloyd, D., Payne, R., Train, C., Williams, D., (eds.), *Victorian Ludlow* (Scenesetters, 2004), 220–1.

19. SA 2740/10: 25 November 1887.

20. *Bridgnorth Journal*, 28 January 1888, 5.

21. SA 2740/10:1885, House Surgeon's Work.

22. *Bridgnorth Journal*, 29 October 1887.

23. *Bridgnorth Journal*, 28 January 1888.

24. *Bridgnorth Journal*, 19 January 1889.

25. BHR, Folder No. 2: Bridgnorth and South Shropshire Infirmary, Report and Balance Sheets for 1889 (booklet).

26. BHR, Folder No. 6: Speech of the Bishop of Hereford at the Annual Meeting of the Bridgnorth and South Shropshire Infirmary, Town Hall, 31 January 1890.

27. The founders of the Bridgnorth Medical Aid Association in December 1890 were: Mr Enoch Sarjeant, Coney Villa, Friars Street, President: Insurance Agent and Office Clerk, Southwell Carpet Manufactory.
Mr Frederick Callant, No. 56 High Street, Vice-President: Hosier and Outfitter.
Mr Walter John Meyrick, Oldbury Terrace, Secretary: Cashier.
Mr Thomas Whitefoot, Jr., No. 36 High Street, Treasurer: Wine and Spirit Merchant.

28. *Bridgnorth Journal*. Taken from various reports including: 20 December 1890; 10 January 1891; 28 January 1893 and 24 February 1894.

29. Bridgnorth Library, Local Studies, Reference No. 942.45037/8, *Through Nine Reigns: 200 Years of the Shrewsbury Chronicle*, 23 November 1972, Medicine, 44; Mate's County Series, Shropshire, 1906, 'Obituary' for a questionable biography of William Thursfield, junior, born Bridgnorth 6 September 1838; died Newport, Jamaica, BWI, 22 April 1918.

30. *Bridgnorth Journal*, 14 February 1891, Correspondence. A letter to the Editor from William Thursfield, MD entitled 'Very Amateur Sanitarians'.

31. *Bridgnorth Journal*, 7 February 1891, 5.

32. *Bridgnorth Journal*, 15 April 1893, 5.

33. *Bridgnorth Journal*, 12 March 1898, Provident Branch at Infirmary.

34. Thompson, Melvyn, *Woven in Kidderminster* (David Voice Associates, 2002), 189–90, Bridgnorth. Founded by Joseph Southwell (1809), H&M Southwell became a limited company in 1890. In 1944 the company was sold to The Carpet Manufacturing Company. Carpet manufacturing ceased in Bridgnorth in 1977.

35. *Bridgnorth Journal*, 15 February 1896, 5. Bridgnorth Medical Aid Association Meeting. Comments by Dr. Rhodes.

36. *Bridgnorth Journal*, 15 April 1893.

37. BHR, *Bridgnorth Infirmary Reports 1896–1920*, (Evans, R.H., Printer, Revised January, 1898), Report and Balance Sheets (1896), Opening of the New Infirmary.

38. BHR, Folder No. 5: *Bridgnorth Journal*, 19 September 1896, 5.

6 FIT FOR THE AGE

1. BHR, *Bridgnorth Infirmary Reports 1896–1920*: Report and Balance Sheets (1896), Opening of the New Infirmary.

2. Royal Institute of British Architects (hereafter RIBA), The British Architectural Library, *The Builder*, 16 December 1893, Competitions, 451.

3. RIBA Library Information Unit. (1) Biographical database for Maidman; (2) *Candidate's Separate Statement* by Maidman for admission as a Licentiate of the RIBA, dated 7 March 1911, by which time he was a Vice-President of the Edinburgh Architectural Association.

4. *Bridgnorth Journal*, 27 April 1895, 5: Laying of the Foundation Stone.

5. BHR, Folder No. 5: Circular *'Tis Sixty Years Since'*, (December 1893) with a line drawing of the proposed new Infirmary on the front page.

6. *Bridgnorth Journal*, 11 August 1894, 5.

7. BHR, *Bridgnorth Infirmary Reports 1896-1920*: Report and Balance Sheets (1896), Opening of the New Infirmary.

8. SA 5586/5/3/27: Apley Park, Survey of Properties, Bridgnorth, North Gate, 102. Written in red 'sold to Infirmary' and undated; also personal communication with Mr. John A. Piper, a descendant of Wilmott (as spelt on a birth certificate of 1884).

9. Permission to view the painting and verify the artist's signature (attributed to either Westcott or Webb) and date failed as the painting was not located. Personal communication: Mrs Judy Nagle's parents, Mr and Mrs Harold Agar, owned the painting that Dr Dickson was 'keen to purchase'. Mrs Nagle donated the painting, in memory of her parents, to the League of Friends in August 1987 which, at one time, hung in an administrative office at the Bridgnorth Hospital.

10. *Bridgnorth Journal*, 22 December 1894, 4.

11. *Bridgnorth Journal*, 27 April 1895, 5.

12. *Bridgnorth Journal*, 22 December 1894, 5.

13. Ibid. 5.

14. I am indebted to Mrs Barbara M. Loudon, a descendant of Miss Frances 'Fanny' Hadfield, for the following inscription upon the jug that is in her family's possession: 'Presented/ to/ Miss Hadfield/ on leaving the/ Infirmary/ by the poor people of/ Bridgnorth/ Jany. 1895'. An early photograph of 'Fanny' in a nurse's uniform, taken in Derby and undated, was also provided by Mrs. Loudon.

15. *Bridgnorth Journal*, 22 December 1894.

16. *Bridgnorth Journal*, 25 March 1899, 5.

17. *Bridgnorth Journal*, 2 March 1895, 4.

18. *Bridgnorth Journal*, 6 April 1895, 8: New Bridgnorth & SS Infirmary. Building matters and a list of builders and their respective tenders including the local builder, Mr. W. Bate, who submitted a tender of £5,247.

19. BHR, *Bridgnorth Infirmary Reports 1896-1920*: Fundamental Rules, 1, (passed 17 September 1897).

20. *Bridgnorth Journal*. Various reports on the Laying of the Foundation Stone of the Bridgnorth and South Shropshire Infirmary, 6, 20, 27 April 1895.

21. Burdett, Henry, *Hospital Sunday and Hospital Saturday*, (1884), 8. BMI Pamphlets, Vol. 28. The University of Birmingham, Special Collections, Barnes Library.

22. BHR, Folder No. 2: Report of the Committee for 1873.

23. *VCH*, Vol. ii, (1973), Population Table, 1801-1961, 220.

24. *Bridgnorth Journal*, 8 February 1896, 2.

25. *Bridgnorth Journal*, 26 September 1896, 5.

26. *Bridgnorth Journal*, 7 March 1896, 8.

27. BHR Folder No. 5: *Bridgnorth Journal*, 19 September 1896: Opening of the New Infirmary. Much of what follows in this section is taken from this report including comments by Mr T.M. Southwell.

28. Ibid. Opening of the New Infirmary.

29. Bynum, W.F., *Science and the Practice of Medicine in the Nineteenth Century* (Cambridge University Press, 1996), 198.

30. BHR, Folder No. 5: Circular *'Tis Sixty Years Since'*, December 1893.

31. *Bridgnorth Journal*, 27 April 1895, 5 and 19 September 1896, 5. See also *The Building News*, 24 February 1899, 269, for the Bridgnorth and South Shropshire Infirmary.

32. Richardson, Harriet, (ed.), *English Hospitals 1660–1948 A Survey of their Architecture and Design* (RCHME, 1998), 5; *Bridgnorth Journal*, 27 April 1895, 5.

33. A remark by the Bishop of Hereford, Dr Percival. Oxford educated, he accepted the Bishopric of Hereford on 16 February 1895.

34. *Bridgnorth Journal*, 27 April 1895, 5. A remark by the Mayor of Bridgnorth, Mr William Henry Beach. Mayoral elections were held annually on either the 9 or 10 November. On 9 November 1895 and 1896, Mr Edmund Martin Southwell was duly elected by his contemporaries as Mayor of Bridgnorth.

35. *Bridgnorth Journal*, 19 September 1896; BHR, Folder No. 5.

36. BHR, *Bridgnorth Infirmary Reports 1896–1920*: Fundamental Rules and Bye-Laws, 1–13.

37. Ibid. 9.

38. BHR, *Bridgnorth Infirmary Reports 1896–1920*: Report of the House and Finance Committee, (1901), II, Outside Nursing, 6.

39. Ibid. 18–19. (See Appendix 2 for Regulations for Private Nurses).

40. *Bridgnorth Journal*, 7 February 1891, 5: Dr Mathias' comment at col. 2.

41. Bank of England Inflation Calculator at: www.bankofengland.co.uk/education/Pages/resources/inflationtools/calculator/default.aspx (Accessed February 2017).

42. *Bridgnorth Journal*, 7 October 1899, 5.

43. BHR, Folder No. 4: Conditions of Sale, House and premises lately occupied as an Infirmary situate in Bridgnorth. Drawn up by Nicholls and Taylor, Solicitors of Bridgnorth and signed over a deep pink 6d stamp and dated 22/3/97.

44. *Bridgnorth Journal*, 1 January 1898: Dictionary of Dates for 1897.

1. National Insurance Act 1911, Section 15 (1) at: http://www.sochealth.co.uk/history/NIA1911.htm (Accessed February 2008).

2. E.T. Sloane, 'An attic window on Dogpole that still marks the beginnings of a great Shrewsbury work. How the old Penitentiary became the first Eye and Ear Hospital', *Shropshire Magazine*, 4, (August 1951), 13–14.

3. BHR, *Bridgnorth Infirmary Reports 1896–1920*, (1900), Outside Nursing, 9.

4. Hallett, G.E.M., 'Dental Education and Provision of Services in the North East of England', in Gardner-Medwin, D., Hargreaves, A., Lazenby, E., (eds.), *Medicine in Northumbria, Essays in the History of Medicine*, (The Pybus Society, 1993), 301–9.

5. BHR, *Bridgnorth Infirmary Reports 1896–1920*, (1905), 3.

6. Roberts, Valerie, *The Story of Much Wenlock Cottage Hospital*, (Preface dated March, 2003), 7–8. No publishing or other details.

7. The Lady Forester Trust, private papers: Llandudno/LL/145.

8. The Lady Forester Trust, private papers: Llandudno/ND/LL/147.

9. *Bridgnorth Journal*, 27 April 1907, 5.

10. *Bridgnorth Journal*, 29 August 1908, 4.

11. *Bridgnorth Journal*, 24 April 1909, 5; BHR, *Bridgnorth Infirmary Reports 1896–1920*, (1909), 4.

12. *Bridgnorth Journal*, 4 February 1911, 5.

13. *Bridgnorth Journal*, 30 May 1914, 5.

14. Cherry, Steven, *Medical Services and the hospitals in Britain, 1860–1939* (Cambridge University Press, 1996), 52.

15. Davis, John, *A History of Britain, 1885–1939* (St Martin's Press, 1999), 101.

16. *Bridgnorth Journal*, 20 May 1911, 5: Correspondence.

17. *The Times*, 3 June 1911, 7, 'The National Insurance Bill, the Position of Hospitals, Fears of Reduced Contributions' at: http://archive.timesonline.co.uk/tol/archive (Accessed May 2008)

18. BHR, *Bridgnorth Infirmary Reports 1896–1920*: Revenue Account, (1912).

19. *The Times*, 3 June 1911, 7.

20. Cherry, Steven, *Medical Services and the hospitals in Britain, 1860–1939* (Cambridge University Press, 1996), 53.

21. *Bridgnorth Journal*, 23 December 1911, 5.

22. Porter, Roy, *The Greatest Benefit to Mankind: A Medical History of Humanity from Antiquity to the Present* (Fontana, 1999), 639.

23. *Bridgnorth Journal*, 13 January 1912, 2.

24. British Medical Association (hereafter BMA), Records and Archives, *BMJ Supplement*, 21 December 1912, 705. Shropshire and Mid-Wales Branch.

25. BMA Records and Archives, *Medical Directory*, Provincial, 1913.
26. *Bridgnorth Journal*, 18 January 1913, 5.
27. *Bridgnorth Journal*, 15 February 1913, 4.
28. *Bridgnorth Journal*, 5 April 1913, 6.
29. *Bridgnorth Journal*, 11 April 1914, 5.
30. *Bridgnorth Journal*, 4 April 1914, 5: 'Bridgnorth and South Shropshire Infirmary, the President appeals for support. Discussion as to adding panel doctors to medical staff'. (Surgical Report, Dr Craig).
31. *Bridgnorth Journal*, 19 April 1913, 5.
32. Ibid. 5.
33. *Bridgnorth Journal*, 4 April 1914, 5: 'Bridgnorth and South Shropshire Infirmary, The President Appeals for Support. Discussion as to adding Panel Doctors to Medical Staff'. (Mr W.J. Meyrick).
34. Ibid. 5. (Mr A.J. Meredith).
35. Ibid. 5. (Dr Craig).
36. *Bridgnorth Journal*, 11 January 1913, 7: Shropshire Panel Filled.
37. *Bridgnorth Journal*, 4 April 1914, 5. (The Revd A. Hodgson).
38. Ibid. 5. (The President, Mr W.H. Foster).
39. Bridgnorth Medical Practice Health Guide, *The History of Bridgnorth Medical Practice*, (Review Publishing Services, undated), 1.

8 War and the Peace unfolded

1. Quoted in Professor Asa Briggs, 'Britain: Lloyd George Takes Over' in *History of the First World War*, Vol. 4, No. 15, 1750–1755, Purnell and Sons (1970) for BBC Publishing Ltd. in co-operation with the Imperial War Museum.
2. *Bridgnorth Journal*, 12 September 1914, 5; 19 September 1914, 5.
3. SA, SC 34/1A1/1: County of Salop War Assistance Committee Minutes, War Refugees, 14 November 1914, 27.
4. BHR, *Bridgnorth Infirmary Reports 1896–1920*: Report of the House and Finance Committee, (1914), 6.
5. Ibid. 6.
6. British Red Cross Archives, *Guide to Records of Auxiliary Hospitals, 1914–19*.
7. British Red Cross Archives, Service Record of Miss Hannah Mary Bailie.
8. *Bridgnorth Journal*, 15 August 1914, 5: Correspondence.
9. SA, SC34/1A1/1: County of Salop War Assistance, Executive Committee Minutes 5 September 1914, 11 re: Bridgnorth District Committee by letter.
10. Ibid. SA, SC34/1A1/1; *Bridgnorth Journal*, 26 September 1914, 4.

11. *Bridgnorth Journal*, 2 June 1917, 5.

12. *Bridgnorth Journal*, 6 March 1915, 5.

13. *Bridgnorth Journal*, 13 March 1915, 5.

14. *Bridgnorth Journal*, 20 March 1915, 4.

15. SA, C21.3, *The Red Cross in Shropshire, An Account of Voluntary Aid Work carried out in Shropshire, January, 1915 – 31st May, 1918.* Transport, 25–7; Wood, Major W. de B., (ed.), *The History of the King's Shropshire Light Infantry in the Great War 1914–1918*, (The Medici Society, 1925), 330. Kindly loaned by the late Mr Maurice Evans, a nonagenarian of Bridgnorth.

16. *Bridgnorth Journal*, 25 March 1916, 5: (Dr W.W. Craig, col. 4).

17. *Bridgnorth Journal*, 3 February 1917, 5; 10 February 1917, 4.

18. *Bridgnorth Journal*, 14 April 1917, 4.

19. *Bridgnorth Journal*, 24 March 1917, 8.

20. SA, C21.3, The Red Cross in Shropshire. Finance, 20.

21. *Bridgnorth Journal*, 29 March 1919, 3.

22. *Bridgnorth Journal*, 6 April 1918, 5.

23. Ibid. 5.

24. I am indebted to Mr Peter Duckers, previously curator of the Shropshire Regimental Museum, The Castle, Shrewsbury for information on those Bridgnorth doctors who joined the Royal Army Medical Corps in the First World War.

25. *Bridgnorth Journal*, 25 March 1916, 5.

26. Ibid. 5.

27. *Bridgnorth Journal*, 25 March 1916, 5. (Dr W.W. Craig, col. 4).

28. *Bridgnorth Journal*, 22 January 1916, 4. Advertisement: Perry and Phillips and the sale, by private treaty, of the residence 'The Grove', West Castle Street, Bridgnorth.

29. *Bridgnorth Journal*, 28 October 1911, 8: Death of F.W. Hewett; BHR, *Bridgnorth Infirmary Reports 1896–1920*, (1911), 3.

30. *Bridgnorth Journal*, 13 January, 1917, 5.

31. *Bridgnorth Journal*, 14 April 1917, 4, col. 5.

32. BHR, *Bridgnorth Infirmary Reports 1896–1920*, (1918), 5, Hamper Scheme.

33. *Bridgnorth Journal*, 24 March 1917, 8.

34. *Bridgnorth Journal*, 26 January 1918, 5: Correspondence.

35. A memorial plaque to Harold E. Welch in St Leonard's Church, Bridgnorth, a Grade II Listed building, now under the ownership of the Churches Conservation Trust.

36. BHR: those 'Consulting Physicians' who preceded Dr William Thursfield, (Jr) at the Bridgnorth Infirmary are derived from the unbound and incomplete Annual Reports. Please note, the dates span missing years:
Dr Bell Fletcher of Birmingham (1842–89 + 1896)
Dr Topham of Wolverhampton (1850–63)
Dr Malden of Worcester (1835–57)
Those annual reports no longer extant are: 1836, 1840/ 41, 1843–6, 1848/ 49, 1855, 1858–61, 1864–71, 1873, 1878, 1885–8 and 1890–5. Dr Thursfield is recorded as a 'Consulting Physician' in the bound *Bridgnorth Infirmary Reports 1896–1920* from 1897–1911, whereupon the post ceased. In 1928 two honorary specialists were introduced to the Infirmary, and a further seven in 1934; all were associated with Wolverhampton Hospitals. Their names and specialities are given in Notes and References, Epilogue, Ref 6.

37. *Bridgnorth Journal*, 29 March 1919, 3.
38. Ibid. 3.
39. Ibid. 3.
40. *Bridgnorth Journal*, 5 April 1919, 3.
41. Thomas R. Oakley, 8 Whitburn Street, Bridgnorth. His correspondence to the *Bridgnorth Journal* (5 April, 26 April and 10 May, 1919) brought responses from Mrs Gilroy (19 April 1919) and John P. Wright (3 May 1919) the retired honorary secretary of the Infirmary, both of whom failed, in their respective ways, to appreciate the grievances of the working classes who wished to be attended by their panel doctors at the Infirmary.
42. *Bridgnorth Journal*, 11 December 1920, 5.
43. *Bridgnorth Journal*, 16 April 1921, 2.
44. BHR, *Bridgnorth Infirmary Reports 1896–1920*, (1920) 3, Report of General Committee.
45. *Bridgnorth Journal*, 16 April 1921, 2.
46. Ibid. 2.; see also 12 February 1921, 5.
47. *Bridgnorth Journal*, 7 May 1927, 5.
48. An appreciation of Dr Wilfred Watkin-Pitchford, by Sir William Thomson, Principle, University of the Witwatersrand, Johannesburg, South Africa, that was sent to the Town Clerk of Bridgnorth and reproduced in the *Bridgnorth Journal* on 9 July 1927, 5.

1. *Bridgnorth Journal*, 10 April 1937, 5. Comment by Lady Boyne at the AGM.
2. *Bridgnorth Journal*, 8 December 1928, 5.
3. *Bridgnorth Journal*, 7 April 1928, 5.
4. *Bridgnorth Journal*, 4 April 1925, 5.
5. *Bridgnorth Journal*, 7 April 1928, 5.
6. Honorary Consultant Staff, all specialists in their respective medical fields, and appointed to the Infirmary, were: Dr G.E. Dyas (radiologist); Dr S.C. Dyke (pathologist); Dr J.H. Sheldon (physician); Messrs E. Deanesley and R. Milnes Walker (surgeons); Mr Wynn Green (ophthalmologist); Mr S.W. Maslen-Jones (gynaecologist); Mr H. Hallchurch (aural surgeon); and Mr E.A. Freeman (orthopaedic surgeon). (*Bridgnorth Journal*, 6 April 1935, 5).
7. *Bridgnorth Journal*, 8 December 1928, 5.
8. *Bridgnorth Journal*, Dictionary of Dates: 6 November 1928; 8 October 1929.
9. *Bridgnorth Journal*, 6 April 1935, 5.
10. *Bridgnorth Journal*, 9 April 1938, 5.
11. *Bridgnorth Journal*, 8 April 1939, 5.
12. *Bridgnorth Journal*, 6 April 1940, 5.
13. Abel-Smith, Brian, *A History of the Nursing Profession* (Heinemann, 1960), 167–9. In summary the Committee eventually recommended a working week of no more than 96 hours per fortnight with one complete day off a week and 28 days' annual leave, with pay, whilst sick pay could vary from one months' to three months' full pay dependent upon the length of service. Higher pay for trained grades was also recommended e.g. resident ward sisters' salaries were placed from £130 per annum whilst resident assistant nurses' salaries were to commence from £50 per annum.
14. *Bridgnorth Journal*, 7 April 1945, front page.
15. Fraser, Derek, *The Welfare State* (Sutton, 2000), 62; Fraser, Derek, 2nd ed., *The Evolution of the British Welfare State* (Macmillan, 1984), 213–14.
16. Klein, Rudolf, 2nd ed., *The Politics of the National Health Service* (Longman, 1989), 7.
17. Fraser, Derek, *The Welfare State*, (Sutton, 2000), 69; Fraser, Derek, 2nd ed., *The Evolution of the Welfare State*, (Macmillan, 1984), 215.
18. Ibid. (1984), 220.
19. *Bridgnorth Journal*, 10 April 1948, 5: 'Last Annual General Meeting of Infirmary State Will Take Over In July'.

Index